Secrets of *the* Best-Run Practices

2ND EDITION

JUDY CAPKO

What Makes Some Practices Stand Out from the Crowd?

GREENBRANCH
PUBLISHING

Phoenix, Maryland

Published by Greenbranch Publishing, LLC
PO Box 208
Phoenix, MD 21131
Phone: (800) 933-3711
Fax: (410) 329-1510
Email: info@greenbranch.com
Website: www.mpmnetwork.com, www.soundpractice.net, www.codapedia.com

This publication is designed to provide general medical practice management information and is sold with the understanding that neither the author nor the publisher is engaged in rendering legal, accounting, ethical, or clinical advice. If legal or other expert advice is required, the services of a competent professional person should be sought.

Printed in the United States of America by United Book Press, Inc. www.unitedbookpress.com

PUBLISHER
Nancy Collins

EDITORIAL ASSISTANT
Jennifer Weiss

BOOK DESIGNER
Laura Carter
Carter Publishing Studio

INDEX
Hearthside Publishing Services

COPYEDITOR
Karen Doyle

Dedication

To my treasured twin sister, Janice Bentz Lyman,
who is kind and caring beyond measure,
and in memory of our sister, Sandra Bentz Woodrum.
She loved deeply and lived a valiant life.

TABLE OF CONTENTS

Your access code is printed on page 218 of this book.

Access code printed on page 218 of this book.

TOOLBOX FORMS

Alpha Numerical Accuracy Quiz
Appointment Power Words Matrix (Chapter 5)
Batch Control Slip
Charting Do's and Don'ts
Clinical Telephone Tracking Incoming Calls (Chapter 3)
Communication Matrix (Chapter 6)
Comparing Key Performance Indicators
Don't Ask These Questions
Employee Benefits Audit Form
Employee Counseling Form
Employee Exit Interview
Employment Agreement Letter
Guidelines For Strategic Planning (Chapter 12)
Individual Human Resource Record
Job Description Questionnaire
Management Skills Audit (Chapter 10)
Meeting Action Matrix (Chapter 10)
New Employee Check List
New Employee Progress Report
On Site Patient Time Study
Past Employer Reference Check
Patient Satisfaction Survey (Chapter 15)
Patient Visit Time Study (Chapter 3)
Payer Performance Table (Chapter 9)
Performance Evaluation Report
Phone Tracking (Incoming calls)
Physician's Retreat Questionnaire
Pre-surgical Financial Arrangements
Problem-Solving Worksheet (Chapter 8)
Productivity Tracking Form
Request For Time Off
Risk-Opportunity Matrix (Chapter 8)
Rooming Matrix - Patient Prep Standards (Chapter 5)
Sample Bio Sketch (Chapter 10)
Sample Discharge Letter (Chapter 6)
Sample EHR Project Timeline Schematic (Chapter 7)
Sample Job Description (Chapter 2)
Sample Performance Standards Worksheet (Chapter 8)
Sample Organizational Chart (Chapter 11)
Staff Survey - How Does Management Rate (Chapter 10)
Team Leader Tips
Telephone Appointment Tracking (Chapter 3)
The Art of Delegation (Chapter 4)
Tracking Log Diagnostic Studies (Chapter 6)
Training Monitor (Chapter 4)
Twelve Point Office Efficiency Test

Acknowledgments

The value of this book is due entirely to those that have so generously contributed to its creation—the many physicians and health-care executives that have sought my services over the years, and those who so kindly permitted me to share their story in these pages, even the few that have remained anonymous. They are all so busy and yet put time aside to be interviewed, review the related portion of the manuscript and provide final approval. It is through their help that these stories remain alive and provide a learning experience for the readers.

Of course, I want to extend my thanks to Nancy Collins of Greenbranch Publishing for providing me with a boatload of opportunities over the years. My appreciation goes out to her team of experts that made this book a reality. Thanks also to the cheering squad—my family, friends and wonderful colleagues—and to those of you that have supported my success as an author by purchasing books and telling others about them. Finally, thanks to an awesome God for all his blessings.

About the Author

Judy Capko is the founder of Capko & Company, a healthcare consultant, speaker and author of the popular book *Secrets of the Best-Run Practices*, First Edition (Greenbranch Publishing, 2006) and *Take Back Time—Bringing Time Management to Medicine* (Greenbranch Publishing, 2008). Judy has specialized in medical practice operations and marketing for more than 25 years, and passionately believes it is by raising others up that we achieve our greatest results. She lives this belief in her consulting by valuing staff members' contribution, giving them the resources to succeed and building patient-centered strategies. Thousands of physicians, administrators and healthcare executives have benefited from her advice and innovative, energetic approach to organizational management, strategic planning and customer service.

Judy has gained national recognition in her field, working with both small and large practices, as well as major academic faculty practices from coast to coast. Contact her at judy@capko.com and www.capko.com/blog

She is a popular speaker for major healthcare conferences and has been a featured presenter at Pri-Med, The Medical Group Management Association, The Professional Association of Health Care Office Management, national specialty associations, regional medical societies and healthcare executive summits, and has been a keynote speaker at corporate healthcare conferences. Judy has been interviewed by and published in over 50 prestigious national medical journals. In addition, she writes a regular column for *The Journal of Medical Practice Management*, *Repertoire Magazine*, *Urology Times* and *Physicians Practice Pearls*. She has also been featured in Sound Practice podcasts (www.soundpractice.com) and has been interviewed multiple times for Reach MD podcasts (www.reachmd.com). Judy serves on the Advisory Board for *The Doctor's Office* and *The Journal of Medical Practice Management.*®

Judy and her husband, Joe, live in Newbury Park, California. They have three adult children, Joe Jr., Christopher and Cheryl, and seven treasured grandchildren.

Stellar reviews from the 1st edition of Secrets of the Best-Run Practices

"Reading the Capko book is like having your own practice consultant on call 24/7."
Marc Wishingrad, MD, Partner, GI Associates, and Assistant Clinical Professor, David Geffen/UCLA School of Medicine

"I can say without reservation that I have been there, done that! The chapters read like a great mystery . . . uncovering the nucleus of the office problems. Judy is the Pink Panther of health care management. Judy presents the problem, solution and implementation plan in a very neat and orderly manner."
Colleen Burgess, CMM, Past-President, PAHCOM (Professional Association of Health Care Office Management)

"The format takes the reader through real life encounters with practices struggling to conquer challenges in their operations and provides solutions to turning the practice into a best-run practice."
Ann C. McFarland, FACMPE, Past President of CA MGMA (Medical Group Management Association)

"As far as I'm concerned, it should be required reading for any doctor who manages their business. Chapter 11 is my favorite chapter. It puts an organized method of focusing on the important numbers of a medical practice: what goes in vs. what is going out."
Brent Greenberg, MD, President, Penn Elm Medical Group

"A physician in practice today can no longer rely on the art of medicine for success. Business is a complex and time consuming chore. This book affords the busy clinician all the tools for success; truly a manifestation of working smarter not harder."
Carol L. Henwood, D.O., FACOFP, Governor American College of Osteopathic Family Physicians

"Every practice has pitfalls to avoid, crises to fix, and goals to meet. No matter how well we think our practices are doing, there is usually room for improvement and trouble always looming on the horizon. Judy's analysis and recommendations are very specific, practical and direct."
W. Lee Wan, MD, Coastal Eye Specialists

"This book should become one of the secrets of your own 'best-run' practice."
Timothy W. Boden, CMPE, Administrator and Editor, FAST PRACTICE

Introduction

During more than 25 years in the business of practice management and marketing consulting, I have talked with thousands of physicians in a variety of healthcare organizations. I have worked with hundreds of practices reaching out for help. Some were in troubled waters and about to sink. Others needed only a few navigational tools to get them back on course. Running a busy medical practice or ambulatory care center in the 21st century isn't easy, and some challenges seem insurmountable. But when the team pulls together, it can move into calm waters and set a new course for its destination.

Rising above the tide and guiding a practice to achieve greatness contribute to a business leader's success. It is why practice executives value continuing education and staying ahead of the curve. It is why they so closely monitor the practice's performance and pay close attention to regulatory requirements that affect the way the practice operates.

Some practice administrators and healthcare executives are driven by the desire to be the best. After all, there's a lot of industry hype these days about "best practices." But what does it take to really be the best, and what are best practices?

The *New World Dictionary* defines "best" as: "The most excellent sort; surpassing all others, most desirable, most favorable and most profitable." It seems a lofty goal to be the best. Many seek it, few achieve it. There is one thing you can count on—even the best can't be the best at everything.

This book will help you on your journey, providing information about practices that have mastered particular (and significant) areas of operation, ultimately improving business performance. It covers everything from the importance of declaring your mission to how to manage both telephones and the appointment schedule; from meeting patient demands and streamlining workflow to improving patient satisfaction; and from risk management to revenue cycle management and improving practice finances.

THE BUSINESS OF MEDICINE

Practicing medicine and running your practice like a business has never been more challenging with practice economics at the top of your concerns, along with the unknown factor (at this writing) of healthcare reform.

The environment in which we do business focuses on protecting patients' rights, keeping up with regulatory requirements, offering the best clinical care available and managing the healthcare dollar. At the same time, everyone involved is supposed to take pride in his or her job, enjoy the work and provide red carpet service. That's a tall order by any stretch of the imagination.

Eroding profits, the emphasis on quality and the desire to serve patients better are primary reasons that medical practices seek to reduce processes and improve efficiency. It is essential for everyone in the practice to accomplish as much as possible in a day. Managers focus on ways to keep staff motivated and productive and patients happy, as physicians strive to provide the best care and service in their specialty. Most of us discover along the way that there is much to gain through sharing the experiences of and lessons learned by other medical practices.

Our peers give us insight and reassurance, enabling us to achieve greater gains. The business of medicine is a constant juggling act where we face new challenges and more demands each day. But just the same, running a medical practice can be exciting and rewarding.

WHY THIS BOOK?

Everyone loves a good story, one that has a few surprises, piques our interest and leaves us feeling good. If we find the story intriguing and it reveals a few secrets, so much the better. This is true whether it relates to our personal life or the work we do. Consultants have an opportunity to participate in so many practices and so many specialties. Most healthcare executives never experience this, and so our insight and personal experiences become as valuable as our technical skills. This book is about some of those experiences and secrets learned along the way.

This book highlights success stories from practices much like yours and answers questions so often asked, like: "How do other practices do this?" "What do you see in other practices?" "Is there a better way to do it?" and "What should we be doing?" *Secrets of the Best-Run Practices* will answer these questions and showcase the best practices. It will share experiences and opinions on what it takes to be among the best. These secrets can often be applied to the practice as basic standards to help it become one of the "best-run" practices.

In over 10 years working in medical practices and managing offices, followed by 25 years of consulting, I have been privileged to help many practices in a variety of specialties and sizes, each with its own set of problems to be solved and goals to be achieved.

This book features some of those practices—spotlighting practices that faced difficult situations and rose above them to find greater success. Perhaps you will recognize something familiar as you read. You may, when reading the book, think, "This is the life I'm living," and discover that there are ways to solve difficult problems and sense new-found hope for your practice.

COMMON THREADS

Best-run practices have many similarities that contribute to their success. These common threads begin with the people that guide the practice. These individuals know who they are, where they want to go and what it takes to get there. There are six distinctive traits found in those that are at the helm of outstanding practices, and these traits contribute to their ability to set a course, guide the crew and reach their destination:

1. **Lead and they will follow.** The leaders of best-run practices encourage people to achieve their best. They recognize the strengths of each individual and build upon them, unlocking each employee's potential. Above all they listen—I mean really listen—to the staff. They listen to their ideas. When possible, they will use those ideas to help them build a better-run practice. They listen to staffers' needs and concerns, and provide guidance and support.

2. **Value the people.** For every ship there is a captain, but the ship never leaves the dock without a crew. The best physician leaders, administrators, managers and supervisors know that. They believe in and understand the value of staff. Simply stated, they depend on staff members and have faith in their capabilities, motivating them to do their best. They involve the staff in setting goals and communicate clearly. They get everyone on board; and when the objectives are reached, they celebrate their successes together. In other words, they share the glory. It is the collective team that makes the practice!

3. **Invest in the practice.** No matter how tight revenue is and how difficult it is to manage expenses, the best-run practices are not afraid to spend money—wisely. Management supports staff growth and job enrichment. In best-run practices, funds are set aside for continuing education at every level. Employees are paid well, trained properly and given the tools they need to do a better job. These practices understand return on investment: exploring opportunities to improve the facility, upgrade equipment and integrate new technology.

4. **Manage things.** The best leaders manage things, not people. They set standards and put systems in place. They gather and manage data to monitor the practice's performance, examine trends and reward those that excel. They make data-driven decisions that keep the practice on course.

5. **Look to the future.** Forward-thinking practices outshine their peers in most aspects. They have administrators and physicians that always see a light at the end of the tunnel. These practices don't live in the past, they live in the now, and they look to the future. They explore change openly and grasp new technology. They are continually learning and challenging their own knowledge base, thinking "outside of the box." They listen, they participate and they make change happen for the greater good.

6. **Remember the basics.** As much as the best-run practices look to the future and remain progressive, they also focus on and respect the basics. They work to keep their practices uncomplicated and their patients happy. They are quick to focus on the basics of quality: getting it right the first time; eliminating unnecessary steps; communicating well; and respecting people, time and resources.

These common threads are distinct from each other, but each plays a role in achieving overall excellence. Together, these elements distinguish top leaders and their ability to inspire high performance, mutual respect, pride in accomplishments and a desire to share the glory.

So what happens when the administrator or physician manager doesn't possess all of these leadership traits? It doesn't mean the practice is in troubled waters, and it certainly doesn't diminish the skills that contribute to the success already achieved. This list of traits can be used as a self-evaluation tool, giving managers an opportunity to assess their management style.

Managers continually mold their leadership skills—there is no perfect leader. Those that excel are always seeking ways to enhance their talents.

Throughout their career, they redefine who they are and how they adapt to a changing marketplace. It's a humbling experience. What are the principles and values that guide those at the helm of the practice? What secrets can be learned from other practices, and what driving forces will be integral in your search to be the best?

ABOUT THE BOOK

Not enough time, not enough money and too many demands. This is the dilemma of medical practices throughout the country as they struggle with the kaleidoscope of complex problems involved with managing a busy medical practice. *Secrets of the Best-Run Practices* provides the inside scoop on how some physicians and administrators addressed the needs of their practice, and when faced with challenges improved critical aspects of their practice's performance.

By reading this book, you will find out what makes some practices stand out from the crowd, as it highlights practices that just seem to have that special touch. For instance, Chapter 1, Mission Possible, will talk about the importance of a mission statement to guide the practice and will profile a few practices that truly understand and live their mission. Chapter 2, The Perfect Receptionist Gets Wired, will introduce you to a star receptionist who performs her job with ease and confidence while at the same time embracing new technologies designed to make her job easier without compromising her first role—making every patient feel special. Chapter 3, Conquering Workflow Problems, discusses a busy group practice's solution to bottlenecks at the front office that resulted in unpredictable and unmanageable workflow. Chapter 4, The Amazingly Productive Doctor, features a physician who has accomplished the art of maximizing his productivity—outperforming his peers around the country.

Chapter 5, Mastering the Appointment Schedule, offers practical solutions to creating a realistic schedule that results in better service, higher productivity and improved patient compliance. Chapter 6, Commonsense Risk Management, emphasizes the importance of structuring a program to reduce risk within the practice and details how a little more attention to your patients can provide more than an ounce of prevention. Chapter 7, Shredding the Paper Monster, features a busy, seven-day a week, 12-physician pediatric practice that successfully converted to a new practice management system and implemented a new electronic health record system.

You can learn a lot from the practice's experience, the commitment that was required and the smart use of resources it employed.

Chapter 8, The Changing Dynamics of Outpatient Academic Practices, talks about how faculty practices differ from the traditional private community medical practice and includes the case study of an academic department's success with changing a culture. Steps on managing the revenue cycle and improving financial results are reviewed in Chapter 9, The Power of Revenue Management, which provides tips on how to maximize charge capture and revenue recovery, including how the emphasis on patient collections has changed in recent years.

The book goes on to share the secrets of what it takes to make good employees great. Chapter 10, Great Employees—The Simple Truth, is loaded with solid, practical advice on obtaining peak performance from your employees. Chapter 11, The Money Crunch, tells a tale of woe about a practice that grew too fast and almost imploded. You will learn how this happened and the steps and commitment that were essential for recovery from this debacle.

Chapter 12, Reshaping the Practice—A New Genre, describes three different practices at a crossroads and what they did to change their destiny. Chapter 13, Smart-Sourcing for the Savvy Practice, provides insight on how a number of practices acquired professional resources by outsourcing some of their office functions in order to get the job done better, achieving remarkable results.

Chapter 14, Starting Over—Yes You Can!, is a real eye-opener. It highlights the very different experiences of three physicians that found themselves in extremely difficult situations after years of practicing medicine, and how they took a risk to make a major career change that resulted in a more satisfying professional and personal life. It offers hope to physicians that may feel trapped in their current position.

Finally, Chapter 15, The Practice of the Future, provides my spin on what will continue to be the focus of leading medical practices, as they face new challenges; apply technology to their advantage; and seek innovative approaches to serving their patients, the staff and the community.

The "Toolbox" available online with the purchase of this book is an added bonus. It is packed with 46 sample forms and tools used in the featured practices. They are yours to modify and adapt to your own practice.

The book highlights some less-than-perfect practices that have made painful mistakes, but overcame them with a no-nonsense approach that you can apply to your practice if faced with a similar situation. Some of the case studies and recommendations may seem familiar and be a reminder of past challenges and obstacles you've overcome. Certainly many of you have dealt with workflow problems, telephone madness and an almost unmanageable appointment schedule that posed a threat to future efficiency, profitability and patient service. It provides a helpful reminder that while problems sometimes seem insurmountable, solutions are just around the corner. Of course this requires the willingness to change, an open mind and flexibility. The real trick is getting everyone on the same page. Read on and enjoy.

Your "Toolbox" forms
in PDF and Word
are available online at:
http://capko.greenbranch.com
Your personal access code is printed
on page 218 of this book.

CHAPTER 1

Mission Possible

A mission statement seems superfluous to many practices, and they just never seem to get around to writing one. But to some practices, it is a part of their passion, defining why

they exist and what makes them different from their colleagues or competitors. Most people have a vague understanding of what a mission statement is and what it is supposed to represent. In all the practices I've worked with over the years, I have not seen many healthcare organizations with a profound mission statement that truly defines who they are and why they exist.

Rather than write a mission statement, most practices define a primary goal. Unfortunately, this goal is not always well thought out and does not distinguish the practice or its services. Many simply focus on providing the best quality service in their specialty. Yet they do not spend time defining what that quality is, nor do they have measurements in place to monitor such performance. I was called into a small practice recently for strategic planning that demonstrates just this problem.

While preparing for their strategic planning retreat, I interviewed the physicians and asked each of them what they believed was the greatest strength of the practice. They all agreed, using different words, that the practice provided the best quality care in their specialty to the community. Yet prior to the retreat, when the physicians completed a form that asked them to circle the committees they were willing to serve on, not one of them circled the quality improvement committee. During the retreat, we spent a great deal of time developing a mission statement and determining what actions the practice would take to truly live the mission.

WHY THE HYPE ABOUT A MISSION STATEMENT?

A mission statement is a short descriptive phrase or sentence that is easy to remember and illustrates the business' goals and purpose. It is used to guide a business, and medical practices, ambulatory care centers and hospitals are indeed businesses!

A mission statement should clearly identify your company to its customer in simplistic, easy-to-grasp terms. Take Disney for example. Walt Disney was clear on his purpose and created a mission statement that stood the test of time: "To make people happy." Most of us would agree that this is being fulfilled throughout the many different Disney venues in the entertainment industry. Just watch your kids light up when they go to one of the Disney parks, or think about the warm and happy feeling you get when watching a Disney classic movie.

3M's mission statement is "To solve unsolved problems innovatively." Post-it Notes is a pretty good example, but you can peel the layers of the 3M organization and find many more examples in the innovative products it has created (and continues to develop) for both business and personal use.

Healthcare professionals may think that it is easier for commercial enterprises to create a *meaningful* mission statement, but this is not the case. After all, what could be more meaningful than going to a medical facility and putting your health in its hands?

Perhaps the following examples of medical practices that are living their mission will inspire you to either revisit your mission and purpose or to take the time to create a mission statement that will clearly define your purpose and drive your organization's success.

CARING FOR KIDS

Valley Pediatrics Medical Group was started by two pediatricians: Jane Weston, M.D., and Andrew Lowe, M.D. They love what they do—take care of children and help make them well. Drs. Weston and Lowe have a passion for their work, and they enjoy the patients. They want the children and their parents to feel good about their choice for pediatric care. If the parents are confident, they are more relaxed when they are dealing with a sick child.

Valley Pediatrics' mission statement is simple: "We joyfully improve healthcare for kids," and joyful they are. Dr. Jane (as the patients and their parents refer to her) told me that developing the practice's mission was fairly easy. "Once we understood the importance of keeping it both simple and relevant to who we are and what we want to do," she said, "we were never short on ideas about how we would demonstrate the mission—most of them involving the physician and staff's interaction with the patients and getting them to smile."

Making Visits Fun

"Our hearts are in our practice and in helping kids feel better, and our patients know that," Dr. Andy told me. "We realized kids do better when they can take their mind off the illness, and we find ways to do that." Whenever a patient has a difficult visit, like getting multiple immunizations, the child is taken to the Prize Room to pick out a wrapped gift, simply marked by an age and sex category when needed.

To keep things more enjoyable around the office, each Friday different nurses don their own, separately identifiable clown costume and entertain the kids throughout the day, making them laugh, reducing anxiety and ensuring patient visits are more fun.

Once a month, the practice randomly selects one day as a theme day. It might be Balloon Day, when every patient gets a helium balloon with a treat tied to the end of it, or it might be Book Day, where each child receives an age-appropriate book designed to support a good and healthy life.

Special Events

Valley Pediatrics also has an annual Thanksgiving party where children are invited to bring a gift that will be collected by an organization that distributes the gifts to children in need. Valley also sponsors an annual artists' contest, where patients can submit a creative story or a drawing. The first place winner receives a $50 savings bond, six tickets to the local movie theatre and $500 donated to his or her favorite children's charity. The top-five runners-up receive practice tee shirts.

Valley Pediatrics is proud of its New Moms' Club. This is a formal program each month where the new moms come in for an education session called "Raising Kids Right" with special speakers on early childhood development, nutrition, fretful nights, and a variety of other topics relevant to new moms. The meeting features a social half-hour with the physicians and office staff, followed by the speaker's presentation and ending with a group discussion and networking among the moms. This program is so popular that new moms make reservations far in advance. Two years ago, Valley Pediatrics introduced a three-part series for parents of kindergarteners that also has been very successful.

Convenient Care

Valley Pediatrics makes treatment convenient for its patients. Today there are a lot of working moms, which can make being up at night with a childhood illness a major problem in the morning. For this reason, the practice adopted extended hours. Valley has grown to six physicians and three nurse practitioners, and assigns one provider to offer a morning walk-in clinic from 7 a.m. to 8:30 a.m. on weekdays so working parents can get their sick child in first thing in the morning. "It reduces parental stress tremendously to know their sick child can get in before they make a decision about going to work or taking the day off," manager Lisa Martinale says. "They may not feel joyful about that trip to the doctor, but they are pretty happy knowing they can get medical treatment for little Hannah early in the morning." Valley Pediatrics also has Saturday hours from 9 a.m. to 1 p.m., reducing weekend anxiety for parents and getting patients on the way to recovery.

"We are serious about healing our patients in a joyful way that helps these children relax and feel good about the doctor that is treating them," Dr. Andy told me. "We are fulfilling our dream every day. It's a joyful place to be. Our staff is happy, our patients are happy, and so are their parents. There is a way to bring enthusiasm and joy into your work—even when you must deal with illness and with parents that have reason to be concerned about the nature of those illnesses."

Attitudes are contagious, and Valley Pediatrics understands that it has the ability to help patients feel better about trips to the doctor and to help the family feel connected. Enthusiasm and a joyful attitude have been the hallmarks of Valley Pediatrics success.

THE SPIRIT-FILLED PRACTICE

Peterson Pierre, M.D., a Stanford-trained, board-certified dermatologist, worked in several derm practices before starting his own practice in suburban Thousand Oaks, California in 2005. During this period of time he noticed two incredibly important issues.

First, the customer service was substandard. "The front office staff just didn't get it," Dr. Pierre told me. He felt stymied as he heard patients frequently complain about poor service, but felt there was very little he could do about it.

Second, he realized patients were dealing with more than their skin problems. Some of them had spiritual issues. Conversations would come up, but there was no way he could address everyone's needs, and his actions were limited. Even though he is a Christian, the practice owners were not. But "God knew the desires of my heart, and (over time) He provided," Dr. Pierre said. The Pierre Skin Care Institute (PSCI) was founded in 2004.

Within two short years, PSCI's gross revenue was more than $100,000 above the national average for dermatology practices in the western region of the United States—quite an achievement and a testimony to its success. It has enjoyed rapid and healthy growth and has remained resilient in the face of the economic downturn of the region.

Dr. Pierre's Mission

The first thing Dr. Pierre did was to "dedicate the practice to the Lord and to His glory." His pastor and the elders of his church prayed over the practice.

His practice's mission statement is "To deliver outstanding medical care with superior customer service in a warm, caring environment, reflecting the goodness of Christ." "I wanted the office to be a temporary safe haven from the chaos out in the world—a place where patients could come and relax," Dr. Pierre told me.

Living the Mission

When Dr. Pierre first called me into his practice, I was instantly struck by the ambience. It resembles a beautiful living room. It is not overstated in anyway, but it certainly has the "wow factor." New patients and visitors continue to comment on its beauty. But more importantly, there is a sense of humility that is apparent in the way that members of the practice treat patients as equals and serve the patients with warmth, grace and sincerity.

During that first visit, I noticed the worship music in the background and saw other signs that I soon learned were representative of how this physician is living his mission and proclaiming his faith. A copy of the mission statement is framed and mounted in both the reception work area and the manager's office.

The practice manager, Angela Souza, does not make hasty hiring decisions. She is cautious and makes sure each addition to the staff will put the patient first and make that his or her first commitment. In addition, each new staffer needs to be someone that can personify the practice's mission by providing the warm and compassionate care that is so integral to what this practice represents.

When problems come up, whether it is an employee issue, a patient service issue or an operational problem, before a decision is made the question is asked: "Will this decision support our mission statement?"

PSCI's word-of-mouth referrals have been tremendous. The patients come from diverse economic and religious backgrounds. "I want PSCI to be a place patients can't wait to return to and can't wait to tell their friends, family and co-workers about," said Dr. Pierre. "People are sometimes hurting, scared, angry and apprehensive when they come to see the doctor. What better way to diffuse this than to greet someone with a warm smile and make them feel at home? And all wrapped up in the goodness of Christ. It's the only eternal value PSCI has and my main motivation."

COMMITMENT TO ELEVATING A SPECIALTY

When I first began to work with SpineCare earlier this year, I was impressed with how its two partners and its associate physicians so clearly understood the practice's mission—its purpose and what an important role it played in decisions that were made about their future. It is a refreshing experience to observe a practice that is so true to its purpose, and in doing so has achieved incredible growth and distinguished itself in the community.

SpineCare was founded by Anthony Houssain, D.C., and is located in the Huntsville region of Alabama. It opened its first office in Madison, Alabama, in 2002 and launched a second location in Huntsville in 2006.

From its inception, SpineCare defied conventional wisdom in the field of chiropractic medicine. Instead of the typical, *alternative* chiropractic model, SpineCare chose to position itself as an evidenced-based complement to the traditional medical model.

SpineCare is committed to the following two principles:

1. Provide treatment, management, and rehabilitation of injuries to the spine from lifestyle, sports and work.
2. Provide the highest standards of care and professionalism while closely adhering to our evidence-based philosophy.

By combining its unique approach with spinal care and rehabilitation, SpineCare can provide self-management strategies as well as focused treatment options, which are functional and effective.

This was vital in differentiating SpineCare from its profession's traditional role. Because of SpineCare's approach, there is acceptance among the physicians in the region, and they refer their patients to SpineCare.

The Practice Evolves

When SpineCare grew from a solo practice to a group practice by bringing in its first partner, Sean Caine, D.C., the dynamics within the clinic, as well as the service model, changed dramatically. "A better understanding of our role within the current medical model emerged, resulting in the vital need for better communication between ourselves, our referring physicians and our community," Dr. Houssain declared. "We needed a mission statement to not only reflect these changes, but to represent SpineCare's ongoing evolution."

When the two partners began developing their revised mission statement, they discovered that the process served as a platform to vocalize the partners' individual and shared ideas, and SpineCare's role in and hope for their profession. "It was a trying yet extraordinary experience, attempting to sum up who we are, what we do and where we wanted to be in just two sentences," said Dr. Houssain. "We realized that SpineCare had carved a niche in providing conservative, evidence-based spine care, filling the void that exists between general practitioners and surgeons."

SpineCare's Mission Statement

SpineCare's mission statement is "To demystify neck and back pain by informing, involving, and empowering our community. We will not compromise quality or compassion to be Alabama's resource for spine care."

SpineCare's mission is conveyed in its commitment to provide services that extend beyond basic treatment, including educational resources and appropriate referrals. "Not using the word treatment [in the mission statement] was deliberate," said Dr. Caine. "There are very few voices for evidence-based or best practices in the management of pain of spinal origin, thus we hope to *manage* and not solely treat." Living the mission is exemplified in the actions of SpineCare's doctors and staff, supported by their marketing efforts and portrayed with their image and reputation in the community.

Drs. Houssain and Caine are selective when inviting another doctor to join the practice to ensure that the integrity of the mission and practice model is not compromised. Through its commitment to live its mission and serve the community, SpineCare anticipates expanding even further by bringing in other complementary services providers to offer additional neck and back treatments.

Professional Image

SpineCare's unprecedented relationship with community physicians has resulted in elevating the image of chiropractic medicine in the Huntsville region. The practice intends to extend this throughout Alabama, and is hopeful that this image will expand throughout the nation over time.

The SpineCare service model is unique to chiropractic physicians with its intent to focus primarily on neck and back care and treatment—a strategy that has allowed the practice to capture physician referrals from primary care and OB-GYN physicians in the area. Not only does this enhance the practice's image, but it further validates the importance of coordination of treatment resulting in better patient outcomes.

SpineCare's website, www.visitspinecare.com, is impressive and professional. It tells the SpineCare story and is a strong representation of what this practice is all about. It features a small video clip of each doctor. These individual vignettes support the practice's mission and elevate the visitors' impression of both the practice and the care they will receive in the non-surgical treatment of neck and spine pain and injury.

Obvious Success

SpineCare has grown from a solo practice with one office to a two-office practice with four chiropractic physicians, and its annual revenue exceeds the national average for chiropractors.

SpineCare enjoys a large referral base in the medical community with 42% of its referrals coming from MDs. SpineCare maintains strong relationships with these physicians, continually striving to communicate its mission, be a resource and expand referrals within the medical community.

Mission Reinforced

Drs. Houssain and Caine are highly motivated and passionate about their mission and are able to articulate their beliefs with ease.

SpineCare's current mission statement defines its position in the medical landscape and encapsulates the doctors' passion in providing vital spine care services to referring physicians, patients and the community at large.

CREATING A MISSION STATEMENT

In creating a mission statement, involve everyone in the practice by getting their input about the practice as part of the development process.

Pick a central theme that is not controversial. Ask yourself and other members of the practice team how they view the practice's mission and what behaviors or accomplishments have been instrumental in forming their impressions.

When you are discussing potential mission statements and begin crafting yours, someone should play the role of devil's advocate and ask pertinent questions about how the message you are creating best represents the practice's purpose and how that purpose will be fulfilled by the practice owners.

For example: if you determine that your purpose is to serve the underserved, how will this be accomplished? Will you:

- Market to a specific low-income segment of the population;
- Sign contracts with a Medicaid program;
- Run a free medical clinic once a month;
- Discount flu shots each fall; and/or
- Develop clinic sites in rural underserved areas?

The commitment to the mission of the practice is demonstrated by action, as witnessed in the case studies presented in this chapter. It is the follow through of your convictions.

Focus on the key attributes of your business to get you to the reality of the practice's mission, based on existing services and products, attitudes and behavior demonstrated, the goals the practice sets each year and how hard the practice works to achieve those goals.

In the end, the customer should know what to expect from your practice, what its values are and what the practice is doing in the community—and these need to be consistent. If you are unable to commit to a consistent program to fulfill the mission and have it realized by your customer, then there's a good chance you haven't developed the right mission.

It can be advantageous to dedicate an entire day or weekend to developing the mission statement and to hire an objective professional to guide the process. Include all physicians, and get input from staff members in this process; if you don't, you will compromise the outcome and may not get the support needed to achieve success.

Companies that have created thought-provoking mission statements that are *on-the-mark* got everyone involved in the process. Start by having each physician and staff member, as well as 25 to 30 patients, fill out a form describing their impression of the practice's purpose. This can be a real eye-opener.

Most importantly, remember to keep the mission statement clear and brief. Once it is created, you should develop the vision—what actions the practice will apply to demonstrate that it is living the mission.

THE SECRETS

1. A mission statement is a core essential in defining the business.
2. Living the mission requires a commitment of physicians and staff.
3. Spread the word by communicating your mission in written form such as on the practice's website and in marketing materials.
4. Review your mission statement quarterly at both management and staff meetings.
5. Discuss the mission statement during new employee orientation.
6. Remember that a good mission statement is crystal clear.
7. Keep your mission alive by posting it in the office and referring to it when making major practice decisions.

CHAPTER 2

The Perfect Receptionist Gets Wired

The role of the receptionist has changed vastly in recent years. More is expected of the receptionist in less time. Ultimately, it is the receptionist's job to make patients feel welcome, while at the same time dealing with and processing a barrage of paperwork. There are unrealistic demands, a relentless work flow and sometimes a lack of adequate training and support. No wonder the turnover for this important (and necessary) position is at an all-time high.

> **KEY FACT:** *Give the receptionist the respect, attention and tools this powerful customer-service position deserves.*

Consider the fact that the receptionist is usually the first person a patient meets—the one that needs to make the patient feel connected to the practice. It doesn't say much for first impressions if the patient's experience is negative or if the patient sees a new face every time he or she comes into the office. Worse yet, if the receptionist is ill-informed and poorly trained, he or she may not be prepared to give patients the assistance they need, and his or her own confidence is likely to plummet.

Too often, broad assumptions are made about the poor quality of receptionists. Managers lament how difficult it is to find and retain good receptionists. They get frustrated with the complaints they hear from the front desk staff and struggle with the unending turnover. The same gripes emerge over and over:

1. Receptionists complaining about the workload demands;
2. Receptionists griping about the way patients treat them;
3. Receptionists asking for more help;
4. Patients complaining about the way a receptionist treats them; and
5. Patients complaining about a receptionist's indifference and lack of sensitivity.

These issues are very real, but who will take responsibility for resolving them once and for all?

Own up to the fact that it's management's responsibility to create an opportunity for each receptionist to succeed and feel satisfied about his or her contribution. If you have high-turnover with receptionists or hear the same complaints over and over, look in the mirror.

It starts with respect—and management doesn't always give much to the receptionist. Not too long ago, I was speaking at a conference and stopped by my publisher's booth. A young, ambitious and intelligent administrator of a 12-physician group practice picked up the first edition of this book and thumbed through it. "'The Perfect Receptionist,'" he said, referring to the name of Chapter 1, "that's an oxymoron!" How sad that he believed this. Surely it would be difficult for a receptionist in such an environment to succeed and take pride in his or her work.

Well I'm here to tell you that it's not an oxymoron. The perfect receptionist does exist—just not enough of them. I've met more than a few; and with the right amount of attention and nurturing, an average receptionist can often be molded and motivated to strive for perfection.

EVERYONE LOVES SUSAN

We all welcome the rare receptionist, the one that just loves her job and shows it. She's sensational. I know her, and her name is Susan. She enjoys every aspect of being a receptionist, and it shows.

I first met Susan years ago when I took on an assignment with a four-physician dermatology group. Susan had worked there for years and was one of the most enthusiastic employees I had ever met.

Last year, Susan relocated to the Midwest and took a position as the lead receptionist for an urban cardiology group. In the practice, there are five board-certified cardiologists, two mid-level providers and a compassionate team of nurses and support staff. Susan is among them. She smiles, she's energetic, she's happy to see you and she most obviously loves her job. Everyone loves Susan because she makes them feel important and she's a joy to be around.

Why is Susan such a joy to be around?

It's not because the work is easy or without demands. It's not because she calls the shots and does only what she wants. It's not because she never has to deal with a grouchy patient. It's because Susan has an important job and has been given the tools to do it right. It's because she knows what her responsibilities are and what is expected of her. She takes pride in her job and what she accomplishes.

Patient-Focused

Susan is not responsible for taking incoming phone calls or scheduling appointments over the phone. Too often, these time-consuming tasks are managed at the front desk, putting pressure on receptionists that are often talking to patients at the same time they get bombarded by incoming phone calls. Susan turned down several such job opportunities before interviewing for her current position at The Heart Center. Without those interruptions, Susan can focus on the patients and give them the attention they deserve. This is an important part of making a good first impression and putting patients at ease. She gives the confused or frightened patient the time and help needed, and builds desirable relationships between the practice and the patient.

Susan's attire is impeccable and professional. She wears a name tag so each person will always remember who they spoke with. She ends each encounter with a patient by asking, "Is there anything else I can do for you today?"

Susan is calm, confident and eager to serve the patients, and she keeps the work moving. In her current position, technology has changed the way she performs her tasks and how she manages her workload. Still, her first responsibility is to greet the patients, respond to their needs and answer whatever questions they may have.

New Patients

One of Susan's priorities is to focus on new patients. Her station is designed with a chair for the patient to sit in while Susan conducts a personal interview to complete the new patient information on the computer. This eliminates the patient making errors on a paper registration form, and expedites getting the patient listed in the system and checked in for the day. However, new patients do have the option of pulling registration forms off the practice's website and completing them in advance. While Susan completes the registration form in real-time, she is developing a warm relationship with the new patients.

By the way, when Susan greets a new patient she smiles, welcomes him or her to the practice and introduces herself with enthusiasm.

SUSAN GETS WIRED

Susan has adapted to the technology that is designed to improve workflow throughout the office. For example, in her previous position Susan generated encounter forms for each patient when they arrived. These forms printed at the nurses' station, signaling the arrival of the patient. Now Susan's check-in process includes *arriving the patient* on the computerized electronic schedule, and the nurses' schedule shows what time the patient arrived. The Heart Center implemented an electronic health record system several years ago, so hard copies of patient encounters don't even exist.

The electronic schedule follows the patient's flow through the center, so Susan can simply look at her computer screen to see what's happening in the clinic at any point in time. She can quickly see who is where: if a patient is in the lab, the exam room or the procedure room. This helps her estimate the other patients' wait time without interrupting the nurses. It is easy for her to monitor patient activity throughout the day and keep patients informed of any delay. When delays are apparent, she is sympathetic and asks if there is anything she can do to make the patient more comfortable. This is particularly important since many of the patients are elderly and can become anxious when waiting to see their physician.

Other aspects of the check-in process have also changed with technology. There is a kiosk in the reception room. Established patients have the option of using the kiosk to check in, which also shows their arrival on the electronic schedule. Patients who choose not to use the kiosk still check in with Susan.

At this point, 35% of the established patients use the kiosk, which allows them to check in and pay both their co-pay and any existing patient balance with a credit card in less than three minutes. If demographic and insurance information has changed, patients are required to check in with Susan. It is interesting to note that quite a few of the senior patients are using the kiosk with ease. This may be because when it was first introduced a staff person was assigned to help walk patients through the process.

The kiosk does not result in established patients being ignored by Susan. Even when they check in at the kiosk, she will get their attention to say hello, give a compliment (if the opportunity presents itself) and even ask a personal question like, "Mrs. Williams, how's that new granddaughter of yours doing?" She understands the importance of small talk in making patients feel important. It works.

Susan uses e-communication to her advantage. If there is something Susan wants the nurse or doctor to know about the patient she checked in, she will send an instant message to that individual's computer, for example: "Mrs. Smith must be seen quickly, she has to be at the ophthalmologist at 3 o'clock." This keeps the clinical staff well informed of what to expect, is accomplished at Susan's convenience and allows her to remain at her workstation. She has a card scanner at her station so insurance cards can be scanned while she is completing or updating patient registrations and verifying information. Technology makes it easier for her to stay at her station and with the patients.

Evolving technology can be one of the more difficult challenges for even the most capable receptionist to deal with. At first, Susan wondered if this added technology would compromise the patient service she traditionally gave and make her seem less approachable. Not a chance with Susan; she's perfect at her job and always makes patients her top priority. She masters technology as each new electronic task in this forward-thinking practice is introduced, and she still focuses on the patients, giving them the attention they deserve.

WORKLOAD VOLUME

Susan's workload is manageable, but the volume is monitored on a regular basis. Management seeks ways to reduce processes and improve efficiency through technology. For example, when new patients schedule their first appointment they are directed to the website where they can become familiar with the practice, understand its mission, review physicians' credentials and scope out the various services the practice has to offer. Patients can review patient testimonials and even obtain a map to the office—eliminating the need for a welcome packet, saving both time and money.

What does Susan do when she's not taking care of patients? She has responsibility for managing and updating the website and responding to inquiries that come through the website. This includes inquiries about the new Healthy Hearts fitness center the practice recently opened for its patients to be able to provide a broader range of services to support a healthy heart.

Management understands the importance of supporting the receptionist, giving her the time needed to give patients high-quality service and the freedom to do it her way.

A NAME BY ANY OTHER NAME

Some practices have multiple staff members at the receptionist station and divide check-in and check-out responsibilities in a variety of ways. Because of this, a practice may choose to have different titles for each of the positions. For example, a practice may choose such titles as "patient coordinator" or "patient services representative" to clarify a separation of responsibilities. I don't believe this is meant to make the position seem more important. I certainly hope not. I think Susan has a very important role, and she makes a terrific receptionist.

THE SECRETS

1. Recognize the importance of the receptionist and the skills required to do the job right.
2. Simplify and clarify the position.
3. Let the computer do the talking and the walking—use instant messaging and e-mail, and gather information online.
4. Remove from the front desk staff the responsibility of managing incoming phone calls or scheduling patients.
5. Monitor workload volumes and demands.
6. Staff appropriately to meet patient needs.
7. Explore opportunities to add technology tools without compromising patient service.

FORM ADDED TO YOUR TOOLBOX:

☞ *Sample job description: Receptionist*

CHAPTER 3

Conquering Workflow Problems

"We need help. Our receptionists are drowning, and the patients are outraged," pleaded Mark Schroeder, the administrator of a six-physician orthopaedic practice in the Midwest. In this practice, some of the biggest problems centered on patients arriving at the office. For starters, it was taking too long to check patients in and out. The physicians were getting behind schedule, which wreaked havoc during the clinic sessions. The patients were disgruntled with the long delays. The receptionists didn't have time to verify patient demographics, and they certainly weren't going to ask already angry patients for money. The receptionists and nurses never felt "caught up," and they were frustrated. So were the doctors. The problems were maddening for everyone, and emotions were running high.

> **KEY FACT:** *Centralize and assign tasks sensibly to reduce frustration, smooth workflow and increase patient satisfaction.*

On my initial visit to the practice, I saw the problems first hand. Four doctors were scheduled to see patients, and there were four lines of patients waiting to check in. As I approached the desk, I discovered each of the four receptionists was wearing a headset, making it impossible for patients to know if the receptionist was on the phone or prepared to assist them. The check-in process was moving at a snail's pace.

WHAT WAS WRONG

Each of the six physicians had his own check-in station, managed by his receptionist. Most of the physicians felt "their" receptionist was the only one that knew their patients, understood what was needed and had the skills to properly manage the appointment schedule. Therefore, their receptionist was the only one trusted to check in patients, schedule telephone appointments, check out patients and schedule follow-up appointments. Nonetheless, the current system was failing both patients and staff.

The receptionists could not give patients the attention they needed and deserved. Each receptionist had a choice: either ignore callers by placing them on hold or letting them drop into the voice mailbox, or ignore the patient checking-in to deal with callers and schedule their appointments.

When phone calls dropped to voice mail, they would linger there for hours before the receptionists found time to retrieve them. Patients calling for appointments would hang up in frustration or leave curt messages, and were forced to keep calling back. The incoming calls were multiplying like rabbits in spring, and patient satisfaction was plummeting.

A patient bottleneck at checkout was aggravated by what was happening back in the clinic. Patients that had already seen the doctor stood waiting for the nurse who was wrestling with paperwork or talking on the phone. These patients were delayed because nurses were taking clinical calls from other patients, insurance carriers and other physicians. In between these calls, the nurses would be calling other diagnostic centers to schedule their doctor's patients. They were bogged down with phone calls and paperwork that hampered patient flow—keeping patients longer in the back office and slowing their move to the checkout counter. As if this wasn't enough, the nurses were even completing disability forms and dealing with workers' compensation adjusters.

The practice habitually ran late with anxious patients waiting for their turn. No wonder staff turnover was rampant and disgruntled patients were speaking out.

THE CHALLENGE

I had seen similar situations before. Too many people were doing the same thing! By centralizing some of these tasks, efficiency, workflow and patient service would improve dramatically. The first step would be to gather data to clarify how serious the problem was and identify underlying factors. Collecting the data would be time consuming, but not difficult. The biggest challenge I anticipated was convincing the physicians to change a system they were comfortable with.

Mark and I both knew getting the physicians to approve a change would take nothing short of a miracle. These orthopaedic surgeons had the "my girl" syndrome. They couldn't imagine anyone but their own nurse and receptionist helping them or their patients. Convincing them to centralize would be a hard sell. So we began building our case.

THE POWER OF DATA

Data talk—they are tangible evidence that helps define problems, predict results and influence the decision-making process. Data should be the foundation for planning and negotiation. Before we could get physician buy-in to change the way things were being done, we needed data that would describe the extent of the problem and the value of redistributing the work more efficiently.

A committee composed of a receptionist, a nurse and the clinical supervisor, headed by the practice administrator, assisted with the project. This core group would be invaluable in convincing staff and doctors of the need for change. The committee met to discuss the extent of the problem and the best way to collect sound data.

First we turned to the systems. A report on the number of new and established patients seen in the office was pulled from the computer's practice management system. The scheduling system's templates showed us the appointment slots reserved for the various appointment types for each physician.

The telephone system generated a report providing call information for every telephone: how many total calls were coming in, how long each call took and how many calls were abandoned. But the report didn't tell us the nature of the calls. So we conducted a study, timing the length it took to schedule 10 separate new-patient appointments and 10 separate established-patient appointments uninterrupted. We also documented how often the receptionists were on the telephone when a patient arrived.

The nurses and receptionists were called on to help us collect data from each point of service—the "moments of truth." These detailed data about the types and volume of various activities allowed for a comprehensive view of the overall workflow problems: The data collected included:

- Number of incoming appointment calls, separating new and established patients;
- Average time for a nurse to complete a patient visit if uninterrupted;
- Number of phone calls dropping to voice mail for the receptionists and nurses; and
- The number of abandoned calls.

Each receptionist was enlisted to document the volume of appointment telephone calls received over a one-week period, including those that dropped into voice mail. Most of the receptionists saw the light at the end of the tunnel and were more than willing to lend a helping hand. They knew we were there to make their job easier.

The information collected would enable us to calculate the volume of calls, determine peak hours and examine the various call patterns for each physician. We anticipated and observed variations based on their individual practice style and patient mix. One problem we discovered was the barrage of calls when staff returned from lunch. The practice shut down the phones during lunch break—at the most convenient time for many patients to call for appointments.

The next step depended on the nurses. A patient visit time study was essential to understand workflow throughout the patient visit. We needed to know how much time was lost during a patient visit and why.

Each receptionist and nurse tracked visits for their physician for three days. A patient visit time study form was placed on the chart of every third patient. Exact time was documented on the form as the patient flowed through each process, from check-in to checkout. This gave us solid information on the cause and effect of existing workflow processes.

Additional data were gathered through interviews and observing this busy orthopaedic practice for several days. The observations were very telling—frustrations mounted through the day, and a series of various types of interruptions and activities hampered workflow and consumed time for nurses and receptionists.

THE FINDINGS

Armed with these data, the analysis began. The investigation provided both predictable and startling results. The demand was pinpointed, and workflow processes were clarified:

- The receptionists each handled an average of 39 incoming appointment calls a day, with a low of 22 and high of 56 on a single day. When tracking time, those that dropped to voice mail (VM) required an additional 1.5 minutes to retrieve the message and return the call:
  - 33 established patients:
    - Direct: 20 at 3 minutes each
    - VM: 13 at 4.5 minutes each

- ▪ 6 new patients:
    - — Direct: 4 at 8 minutes each
    - — VM: 2 at 9.5 minutes each
- Sixty-five percent of the telephone requests for appointments occurred between the hours of 9:00 AM and noon.
- Abandoned calls spiked between 12:15 PM and 2:00 PM, accounting for 37% of the total abandoned calls.
- Monday and Friday mornings reported the highest call volume.
- Eighty percent of the patients arrived within five minutes of their scheduled appointment.
- Check-in for an established patient was taking an average of six minutes.
- New patient check-in required 9.5 minutes.
- The receptionist was free from the phones to greet patients on arrival only 25% of the time.
- Patients were roomed as early as five minutes or as long as 52 minutes following completion of the check-in process. On average, the delay was 26 minutes.
- The peak times for bottlenecks in the front office were directly related to the peak time for incoming phone calls and were most severe between 10:30 AM and noon, and again between 2:00 PM and 2:30 PM.
- The peak times for bottlenecks in the clinical setting were in the late morning and again around 4:30 PM.
- Physicians arrived in the exam room an average of 33 minutes after the appointment time for established patients and 39 minutes for new patients.
- The time to schedule outside studies delayed patient checkout by five minutes, but created a secondary delay as the nurse was detained from rooming another patient.
- The time span between conclusion of the doctor's visit and completing in-house studies was 45 minutes. Many times, patients were held up in the sub-wait station, as staff conducting the diagnostic studies got backed-up.
- Scheduling templates showed that often two or three physicians would be seeing new patients at the same time, creating a backlog with x-ray and ultrasound.
- When patients came out of the exam room, one out of three waited for assistance in scheduling studies while the nurse finished a phone call.

- Each nurse had a daily average of nine calls from workers' compensation insurance adjusters.
- Each nurse scheduled an average of 11 outpatient diagnostic studies each day, 8 of these requiring pre-authorization.
- On average, 18 patients were seen for each morning session and 21 for each afternoon session. This meant each receptionist was checking-in and -out an average of 39 patients, and 6 of these were new.
- The patient checkout process averaged 6.5 minutes.

Our investigation indicated that it would require two full-time schedulers to manage the volume of telephone appointments once dedicated schedulers were in place. We also thought that the practice's website should be enhanced so that new patients could pre-register online, and a number of existing patients could schedule their own appointments. These website enhancements would considerably reduce the call volume for the schedulers.

Because they would be relieved of telephone scheduling, the receptionists would have an additional 2½ hours a day to dedicate to receiving and processing patients during clinic sessions. This added time would allow them to adequately review patient demographics and update insurance information. On the checkout side, training would be provided on collecting over-the-counter (OTC) payments, both co-pays and outstanding patient balances.

Preventing multiple physicians from seeing new patients at the same time would level out the demands on in-house diagnostic studies and help improve patient flow in the clinic. Combined with freeing nurses from clerical tasks, this would keep the sessions moving and open up additional time. Nurses could then be assigned the responsibility of auditing each patient's charge ticket to ensure no charges were dropped and diagnoses were recorded.

THE REMEDY

With data in hand, the solutions were clear. If the workload was redistributed through task-related centralization, the majority of the existing flow problems could be solved. The receptionists and nurses could now ensure charges were captured, payments were made and demographics were updated. With proper training and clear expectations, greater efficiency and profitability could be expected.

The preliminary action plan was crafted:

1. Remove telephone scheduling from the front desk receptionists and centralize.
   a. Assign two receptionists to be full-time schedulers and relocate them to a quiet location.
   b. The four remaining receptionists would be responsible for each of the six physicians when they were in session. This would not be difficult as there were never more than four physicians in session simultaneously, and 50% of the time only three physicians were in session at one time.
2. Provide telephone coverage during the lunch hours.
3. Eliminate nurses obtaining insurance authorization and scheduling outside diagnostic studies.
   a. When the fourth receptionist was not in sessions, she would obtain insurance authorizations and schedule all the outside diagnostic studies that had been ordered.
4. Remove clerical duties from nursing by reassigning completion of disability and workers' compensation return-to-work forms to medical records staff. Begin research on the potential to automate these processes.
5. Train staff appropriately for the new tasks to be assumed.
6. Establish daily collection goals for OTC payments.
7. Change the physician scheduling templates to stagger new-patient visits.

Because his nurse was near and dear to each physician's heart, getting the support for change would be more than a little difficult. However, support from the top was essential. The key was getting one physician to endorse the new workflow model and change in staffing responsibilities. Past experience predicted that if we succeeded with converting one physician, a commitment from the other physicians would soon follow.

SEARCHING FOR A CHAMPION

Our first charge was to identify the doctor that would champion our cause and be willing to lead the pack. One physician, Arthur James, M.D., stood out. He was the most forward thinking and decisive of the group. He was also influential with the other physicians. At a meeting to present the data to the remaining physicians and solicit their support, Dr. James played a key role in gaining their confidence and impressing them with the expected gains that could be achieved. He was a master at overcoming objectives and obtaining consensus.

When the evidence was laid out and the plan was presented, the doctors quickly saw the advantages. They knew there was a solid rationale behind our recommendations, but still feared an overall loss of control. Mark and I explained that they could set up their own protocols for scheduling. The doctors could also have input as we developed the training modules for scheduling. A meeting with each physician and the scheduler would take place before the switch was made, and the transition would be unhurried and methodical. Morning huddles with involved staff would begin as soon as the program was launched. Regular meetings would be scheduled during the first 90 days to make sure each physician's needs were being met and problems were quickly solved. Convinced the plan was sound, the doctors approved our plan, and we put it in motion.

MAKING IT HAPPEN

The committee had a lot of planning to accomplish before the transition could begin. The schedulers were added to our committee to solidify their commitment, help us finalize the plan and assist with a smooth transition.

The pre-launch planning took on a life of its own. I headed this effort with the assistance of the administrator and the support of the planning committee. There were planning meetings and interviews. Flow charts and training guides were developed. Job descriptions were revised and implemented. There were telephone scripts, practice sessions and more meetings. We anticipated some resistance, but with the support of their peers that served on the committee, most of the employees accepted our plan with little resistance.

A system was developed to monitor the number and length of telephone calls and to measure the scheduling demands against the capacity of the two schedulers. We needed to follow our progress, know the staffing needs and make any necessary adjustments.

At last, the detailed action plan was ready for implementation. Because the committee members had been actively involved in the development of the model, they were enthusiastic and influential in bringing the remaining staff on board. It didn't take much for staff to visualize how the new workflow model would improve their life on the job—creating a better work environment and manageable workload. The crowning glory would be an end to disgruntled patients. They were about to see all this become a reality!

There were some adjustments that needed to be made during the first few weeks and quite a bit of handholding. There were morning huddles with physicians, receptionists, nurses and schedulers, during which time they would discuss any issues from the previous day, review the daily schedule and prepare for any potential problems that might emerge. At the end of two weeks, the physicians and staff members involved in the process met with the committee to review their progress and discuss any suggested modifications to the plan. In general, everything was on track and moving forward.

REAPING THE REWARDS

Within 60 days of launching the new workflow model, staff and physicians were touting its success. Patients were roomed on time, and the work was flowing. There was no grumbling from patients or staff. Communication was greatly improved. There were fewer interruptions and no disruption! The real bonus was getting out of the office on time. One would be hard pressed to argue with this type of success.

When it comes to patient care and related workflow, this practice is ticking like a fine Swiss clock. The fog of confusion and chaos has disappeared, replaced by a streamlined system that is seamless in meeting the needs of physicians, staff and patients.

The receptionists' productivity has skyrocketed. They now have time to put new-patient demographics in the computer and update changes for existing patients. The benefits are seen in the insurance department, as rejected claims have diminished, improving cash flow. At the same time, cash flow has been given an additional boost because the receptionists now have time to collect OTC payments from patients. In fact, OTC payments increased by 100% within six months.

The nurses are able to assist their patients as they come out of the exam room. Paperwork is processed quicker, and patient care is timely. Schedulers are making appointments the first time around. They have mastered the process. They have time to pre-register the patient properly and with more detail. Errors in pre-registration have dropped dramatically.

Bottlenecks and patient complaints are a thing of the past. As an added bonus, the new workflow model has done a lot for team building. The employees now depend on each other to get the job done and care for the patients. Morale has never been better!

THE SECRETS

1. When complaints are chronic, address them.
2. When volume demands it, centralize functions and streamline processes.
3. Minimize front office interruptions.
4. Keep telephone lines open during the lunch hour.
5. Remove clerical tasks from nursing staff.
6. Centralizing doesn't take additional staff.
7. Patient flow problems reduce productivity.
8. Centralization improves teamwork.
9. When an administrator and consultant team up, the results can be amazing.

FORMS ADDED TO YOUR TOOLBOX:

∞ *Telephone Appointment Tracking*
∞ *Clinical Telephone Tracking*
∞ *Patient Visit Time Study*

CHAPTER 4

The Amazingly Productive Doctor

Time and productivity go hand-in-hand. For years, I've listened to physicians tell me how difficult it is to manage their time. They are continually and equally frustrated with not enough time and dead time—the time they are in the office, expecting to see a patient, and the exam room is empty. Through many consulting experiences and years of examining medical practice operations, I have come to believe these two time problems are equally important. After all, if you don't have enough time, it is difficult to manage the time you do have! On the other hand, if you have dead time, it's cause for concern and will result in loss of productivity and less income.

KEY FACT: *Delegate tasks that do not require your expertise, and your productivity will climb at amazing speed.*

Physicians' time is often eroded because they take on things they shouldn't and the staff should! When conducting site visits, it is common to observe physicians consumed with tasks that could, with little effort and planning, be delegated to the staff. Physicians need to ask themselves, "What am I doing that eats away at my time and doesn't require my skills or judgment?" When these tasks are shifted to employees, doctors can improve their productivity, and just maybe they will actually get out of the office on time.

For many physicians, delegating is easier said then done! There are a number of reasons physicians and administrators fail to delegate, some more common than others:

- A lack of confidence in the staff's capabilities;
- Failure to train employees to assume additional responsibilities;
- The "my way is the only way" syndrome;
- It's a habit that's never been addressed;
- Fear of losing control; and
- Fear of compromising the outcome.

Most physicians, if they set their mind to it, can delegate more and enjoy the time they gain and the benefits it brings them. When staff members are well trained and understand what the physician needs and expects from them, they keep patients moving and everyone works in "real-time." Working in real-time means doing today's work today. This simplifies the day at the office and leaves less clinical work behind.

When physicians want to know what they can do to improve their time management and clinic performance, I am reminded of a long-time client of mine. There's a lot to be said for the way this practice runs its clinic sessions and spends its time.

MAKING TIME COUNT

Coastal Allergy Care, a southern California adult and pediatric allergy practice, is progressive. Staff members always look ahead to see if they can do things better, investing in tools and technology to improve service to their patients while at the same time making their jobs easier. There are two physicians and a full-time physician assistant (PA), with three offices strategically positioned throughout the region.

When problems puzzle members of this busy practice or they feel direction is needed, they don't hesitate to seek professional help. However, when it comes to optimizing physician productivity no help is needed. The practice shines, and there is much to learn about how it does this.

Coastal Allergy has it wired! The smart use of ancillary staff and effective delegation make for smooth clinical flow and good physician time management. I have been amazed at its ability to make the most of each day. This has allowed the practice to reach productivity numbers that far exceed the average allergy practice.

Coastal relies on its entire clinical staff to keep the doctors and PA moving and patients cared for. They complete the day's tasks in real-time so work is completed at the end of the day. Coastal orchestrates clinical sessions with incredible efficiency and productivity. This was the case long before it converted to electronic health records, which gave Coastal the ability to become even more efficient. This additional technology reduces paperwork, provides easy access to information and further enhances productivity.

THE CLINICAL FLOW

This is what I saw as I observed Lewis Kanter, M.D., the practice's founder, and his clinical staff as they went about their day. There are three nurses working with the doctor during his clinic session. Two are shadowing with him, while the other is performing skin tests, providing allergy shots for other patients and lending whatever support is needed.

These nurses not only perceive the needs of the doctor, they perceive the needs of each other. One nurse picks up where the other leaves off. It's amazing to watch. It's like a dance, and it is often orchestrated with very little dialogue. It's obvious that this clinical staff is skilled and has been well trained. They are confident, know what needs to be done and support the physician. They are working to their potential and are given the opportunity to enrich their knowledge and skills—so they can better serve the practice and the patients.

One nurse will escort the patient to the exam room, complete the history taking and prepare the patient for the exam, documenting all this on the computer in real-time. Computers are everywhere—in each exam room, at the nurses' station, in the doctors' offices and in various locations in the business office.

When a doctor is ready to enter the exam room, he can be assured that needed information will be available on the computer terminal. Just as importantly, when he goes into the exam room, a nurse will follow him. The physician reviews the history and moves on to examine the patient, at which time the nurse will sit at the computer. This allows the doctor to focus entirely on the patient. As he completes the exam, and talks about the findings, the nurse scribes, completing the chart documentation. This enables the patient to hear what the findings and impressions are. The process continues as the treatment plan is discussed, studies are ordered and prescriptions are written.

When the physician completes the visit, he is able to leave the exam room, departing with ease; moving on to the next patient, accompanied by another nurse. The first nurse stays with the patient to complete the visit and give the patient instructions. The nurse then goes on to perform whatever diagnostic tests are ordered, posts the visit charges in the computer and sees that the patient receives the proper patient aids and education materials. This is all accomplished while the physician moves on from patient to patient, making the most of his time and using the staff to his advantage. The patients love this approach to their care. They never feel rushed, and they experience a team of people looking after their needs.

New patients are often in the office for up to two hours, having diagnostic procedures and skin tests after the physician consultation. Patients don't mind—because then they don't have to come back for a separate visit for the skin tests and will get into a treatment regimen that much sooner.

In addition to scribing the patient's history and exam results, nurses assume responsibility for entering the visit and diagnostic code into the computer. This is a great concept, because the nurses are in the exam room throughout the visit, hear the discussion between patient and doctor and know exactly what services have been performed and ordered.

When the patient reaches the exit station the charges are already posted, and the instructions for scheduling the next appointment have been documented. There is no need for a receptionist to leave his or her station or get on the intercom with a nurse to track down a charge ticket. This eliminates interruptions, reduces processes and speeds up workflow.

The main facility easily accommodates the ability to glide through the office session. With seven exam rooms and no more than two providers in session at the same time, it is possible to extend the patient visit to include skin tests and diagnostic studies without impeding patient flow or the physician's time.

The goal is to eliminate down time for the physicians and the nurse practitioner. From a financial perspective, they are the most valuable players on the team. With a staff that keeps the flow, they are able to capitalize on this without compromising patient care or the quality of service. This model is practical, and it makes sense.

EVERYONE BENEFITS

What does the practice gain by this team approach to patient care and physicians delegating so much in the clinical setting? For starters, more patients are seen in less time, and they aren't kept waiting.

Members of the staff enjoy their jobs and work well together, which is evident by their longevity. The average tenure for the nurses at Coastal Allergy is more than 10 years. This is a tribute to the physicians and nursing supervisor, Ketty Owens, R.N. Ketty has been with the practice since its beginning. Since the cost of replacing an employee is estimated to be as much as one year's salary, reduced turnover contributes to the bottom-line.

Next, patients are well informed, and it takes less time to diagnose and resolve their clinical problems. The nonverbal communication from the clinic to the front office saves time and reduces frustration. It also reduces the potential for missing charges, missed instructions or failing to schedule a follow-up appointment.

Since the physicians and staff work in real-time, they are not plagued with batches of work that need to be completed at the end of the clinic session. In the end, patients and staff are more satisfied; there is greater productivity and higher profitability.

NUMBERS TALK

Overall, Coastal Allergy Care outperforms allergy practices nationwide, as demonstrated by the productivity performance measures (per full-time equivalent [FTE] physician) shown in Table 1.

TABLE 1. Coastal Allergy Care Productivity Performance Measures*

2008 Statistics	Coastal Allergy Care	NSCHBC
Gross charges	$1,637,559	$1,085,020
FTE staff	6.75	6.09

*per FTE physician
FTE = full-time equivalent; NSCHBC = National Society of Certified Healthcare Business Consultants.

Coastal Allergy's gross charges are 51% higher than the median earnings reported by the National Society of Certified Healthcare Business Consultants (NSCHBC). Coastal reports an additional 0.66 FTE than the NSCHBC average, but this slightly higher level of staffing pays off with far greater physician productivity. Coastal generates greater than $500,000 more in per physician charges than the average reported by NSCHBC, making the additional staff a great investment.

These impressive numbers substantiate the economic benefit Coastal Allergy enjoys due to the highly productive clinical model it employs. It is worth noting that Dr. Kanter is the highest producer for his group, yet is only in clinic session an average of 24 hours a week.

LESSON LEARNED

Sometimes a practice focuses too much on the physician/staff ratio, when additional staff just might be the right prescription for improving practice performance. When staff members are used wisely and doctors delegate more, productivity rises, resulting in healthier profits. At a time when the healthcare dollar is continually being squeezed, this is no small feat. The old adage is true, do what you do best and leave the rest to someone else.

THE SECRETS

1. Take a critical look at how you manage time.
2. Train staff members to meet their potential.
3. Delegate tasks that do not require your skills.
4. Work in real-time.
5. Adding more staff can increase clinical productivity.
6. Optimize exam room utilization and clinic flow.
7. Develop a cohesive clinical team.
8. Improve physician productivity to serve patients better and increase revenue.

FORMS ADDED TO YOUR TOOLBOX:

↪ *Training Monitor*
↪ *The Art of Delegation*

CHAPTER 5

Mastering the Appointment Schedule

KEY FACT: *Stay on time and work in "real-time" with scheduling techniques that meet patient demands.*

All's well that ends well, but sometimes the road to get there has some unexpected twists and turns. Such is the way when it comes to mastering the appointment schedule. Over the years, most medical practices, regardless of their size or specialty, have struggled in search of a way to fine-tune the appointment schedule. Somehow it never seems quite right. The doctor doesn't stay on schedule and rarely gets out of the office on time. When this happens, everyone pays the price: the physicians, patients and staff. Unfortunately, it's not uncommon.

For some practices, managing the appointment system seems like an impossible feat. The phone rings off the hook with patients that need appointments, some more urgent than others. Every day, staff members end up double-booking sick patients when the next "real" opening on the books is three weeks away. Suzanne Johnson, M.D., a busy primary care physician from Texas, experienced these same problems. She struggled with the way patients were scheduled. There were never enough hours in the day, and patients sometimes waited weeks to get an appointment. Adding a mid-level provider was helpful, but it didn't solve the problem for this popular physician. Patients seemed willing to wait to see her, despite their frustration at the long delay. The practice tried a variety of techniques to fix the problem, but just couldn't get a handle on managing the appointment system. Finally Dr. Johnson looked for a consultant to examine the situation and come up with a solution.

LOOKING AT THE INDICATORS

I began the investigation with a search for the next available appointment and discovered that the first opening for an established patient was in eight days, with 18 days for a new patient. If someone wanted an annual exam, the wait was 100 days. A review of the previous week's schedule revealed a pattern of double-booking three to five appointment slots each day. The receptionist told me there was no other choice. Patients that didn't schedule because of the long wait sometimes ended up calling back in a few days because they didn't get better and "had to get in." Sick patients were getting crammed into an already full schedule. It didn't take a genius to realize that the demand for appointments far exceeded existing capabilities.

Next, I observed the clinical staff members working through their day. The reception and exam rooms were full. The physician and nurse practitioner fell further and further behind. In an attempt to get back on schedule, they let their charting go until the end of the day and ended up leaving a stack of work behind for the next day.

When I clocked the wait time for patients, it averaged 35 minutes—from scheduled appointment time until they were actually roomed, coupled with an additional wait of at least 15 minutes once they were in the exam room. No wonder the staff welcomed the no-show patient. With this kind of backlog, they rarely got out of the office on time. Staff members voiced concern about how much overtime they were putting in.

The findings were telling. The classic symptoms of an unmanaged scheduling system were a reality for this hard-working practice:

1. Demand greater than access, delaying the time it takes for patients to get an appointment;
2. Frequent double-booking of appointments;
3. More than an occasional no-show or late cancellation;
4. Long wait times for patients once they arrived in the office;
5. Physician getting out of the office late, mid-day and evening;
6. Charting incomplete at the end of the day; and
7. Continual staff overtime.

GETTING TO THE ROOT OF THE PROBLEM

Now it was time to dig deeper. I proceeded by examining 30 random daily schedules from the previous three months, looking for underlying factors and getting answers to these critical questions:

- How many patients were actually seen each day?
- Were there variables in the daily patient load?
- Was the demand greater on specific days or particular times of the day?

- What trends were contributing to the overall problems?

The analysis revealed erratic scheduling patterns, but several trends were detected. Typically, more patients were double-booked in the late mornings and late afternoons, and nearly twice as many work-ins were added to the schedule on Mondays. The cancellations and no-shows were scattered through the day and throughout the week, elevated slightly on Fridays. The missed appointments averaged at least seven a day, nearly double the amount of work-ins. The variables in daily production when both providers worked ranged from a low of $2,836 to a high of $3,984, more than a 40% differential. If the high of $3,984 became the benchmark, this practice would realize a substantial gain in net revenue.

The physician's amount of time out of the office impeded overall production. Even though Dr. Johnson's typical schedule consisted of eight half-day sessions a week, with a day off at mid-week, she averaged three additional sessions off per month for various personal and business reasons. This did not include the seven holidays and six weeks out the previous year for vacation and continuing education.

I reviewed the existing scheduling templates to assess how effective they were. There were four different types of patient visits being scheduled:

1. New patient: 30 minutes;
2. Established patient: 15 minutes;
3. Pre-employment physical: 45 minutes; and
4. Annual physical: 60 minutes.

I needed to determine whether these time slots were realistic. How much time did each of the appointment types "really" need, and did the physician and nurse practitioner require the same amount of time?

For a period of 10 days, the nurses and the providers marked the charge ticket for each patient seen in the office. The nurses indicated the type of patient visit, and both the physician and nurse practitioner documented the actual time they spent with the patient. This information helped determine how realistic the existing templates were and if they needed to be revamped.

The findings revealed that the physician spent less time with patients then the schedule indicated (Figure 1). This held true for the nurse practitioner as well, with the exception of established patients. The greatest disparity for both providers was the annual physical, where the schedule dedicated 60 minutes, far more than either provider required. Many of the

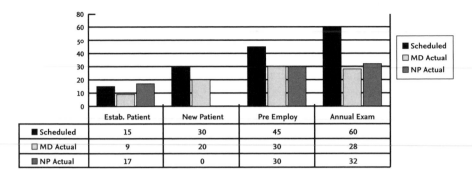

	Estab. Patient	New Patient	Pre Employ	Annual Exam
■ Scheduled	15	30	45	60
☐ MD Actual	9	20	30	28
■ NP Actual	17	0	30	32

FIGURE 1. Time dedicated to each patient type.

work-in patients presented with one symptom: a rash, earache, mole check or common cold. These patients required less then 10 minutes of the provider's time.

The traditional 15-minute incremental appointments just weren't appropriate and didn't provide the flexibility needed to match the actual time providers were spending with patients. Shifting to a schedule with 10-minute increments and revising the appointment time parameters would give the practice needed flexibility. Greater capacity and improved access would follow.

I then asked the receptionist to track the number of patients that were not being accommodated when they called and requested an appointment. For 10 days she kept a log that revealed five to nine patients that could not be fit into the schedule each day. Some of these patients would simply forget about it, but for others it resulted in telephone messages for the doctor and "telephone medicine."

Additional data were obtained from the practice management system to capture the monthly volume of new patients, established patients and patients needing annual exams seen by each provider. This helped clarify how to structure the new templates, based on volume and patient type.

THE FINANCIAL IMPACT

The lost revenue from no-shows and late cancellations was assessed by calculating the average visit charge, multiplied by the average number of lost appointments, subtracting the revenue gained from the double-booked patients. The estimated annual loss of revenue for missed appointments turned out to be more than $125,000. This certainly got the attention of the physician.

TABLE 1. Time Out of Office Comparative Study

	Vacation CME	Holidays	Cancelled Sessions	Total Sessions Out	Above Typical PCP	*Estimated Lost Revenue
The practice	6 weeks = 48 sessions	7 days = 14 sessions	30 sessions	92	38	$62,774
Typical PCP	4 weeks = 32 sessions	7 = days 14 sessions	8 sessions	54	N/A	N/A

*Lost revenue calculated based on primary care average charges from the Society of Medical-Dental Management Consultants/National Association of Healthcare Consultants 2004 national statistics. CME = continuing medical education; PCP = primary care physician.

Additional revenue of more than $62,000 could be captured if Dr. Johnson worked the same number of sessions as the typical primary care physician (Table 1).

The unmanaged schedule also contributed to the cost of overtime wages for the practice. Each receptionist clocked in an average of 15 hours a month in overtime, and each nurse as much as 22 hours per month, for an estimated $72,000 a year.

The annual financial loss was projected to be more than $250,000 a year. There were other considerations that cost the practice as well. First were patients, both new and established, scheduling elsewhere because of poor access. These patients were unlikely to return, representing a long-term loss to the practice. Second, the unmanaged scheduling system resulted in less-satisfied patients, generating word-of mouth damage to the reputation of the practice and loss of future referrals.

DEFINING THE OBJECTIVES

The analysis pinpointed the impact of an unmanaged appointment schedule and crystallized in everyone's mind the issues that needed to be resolved. Three primary objectives were outlined.

1. Improve access
2. Develop a manageable scheduling system
   a. Create valid templates
   b. Balance demand with capacity
   c. Stay on time
   d. Reduce no-show and late-cancellation rates
3. Improve time management

    a. Stay on time

    b. Reduce overtime

Staff buy-in was critical to accomplishing these objectives. Achieving the stated goals required a dramatic shift in the way patients were handled and how they were scheduled. It took a leap of faith for Dr. Johnson and her staff to imagine balancing demand with capacity, staying on schedule and getting out of the office on time.

Ten more patients could be seen each day if no-shows were reduced to a minimum and a tighter scheduling system was developed. Furthermore, access would improve immediately, and the need to double-book would soon vanish. This would go a long way toward getting control over the scheduling system and getting everyone out of the office on time.

MASTERING THE SCHEDULE

Providers were spending between 9 and 32 minutes with each patient. Some of these patients had a simple ear infection and others had chronic conditions and multiple health problems. The new template needed to have the flexibility to meet these variations. Based on the objective data collected and meetings with the nurses and the providers, three types of appointments were developed—"quik-chek," standard, and complex—based on 10-minute increments up to 30 minutes (Table 2).

Implementing these appointment times and time parameters, along with better management of missed appointments, would yield sufficient gains to hold slots for same-day appointments. This would enable the practice

TABLE 2. Types of Appointments

Quik-Chek (10 minutes)	Standard (20 minutes)	Complex (30 minutes)
• Single symptom — Rash/mole — Ear infection — Blood pressure check • Simple recheck • Minor complaints	• Multiple symptoms • Infections • Established patient with chronic problems • Monitoring patient with multiple problems • New patient with minor complaints	• Annual exam • Pre-employment physical • Established patient with complications • New patient with chronic or major complaints

to adequately accommodate new patients and manage the existing patient load appropriately.

A modified open-access system emerged—a system that would accommodate appointments the same day patients requested them. The bulk of pre-scheduled appointments were expected to be for new patients, annual exams and re-checks. To avoid the historical Monday crunch, employment physicals and annual exams would not be scheduled on Mondays. This would result in improved workflow and better time management.

When finalized, the new template placed a hold on 22 10-minute appointment slots per day, releasing them at noon on the prior day. A number of the openings were concurrent, allowing staff to schedule quik-cheks or standard appointments, depending on the needs of the patient. These open slots would go a long way in meeting the historical pent-up demand that kept as many as nine patients a day from getting appointments in the past and the practice of double-booking an average of four patients a day. Besides this, the practice would be better positioned to add new patients, handle growth and manage the day.

In order to accommodate pent-up demand and improve access immediately, the providers were asked to expand their daily schedule by one hour for the first six weeks to eliminate a future backlog. At the end of the six-week period, it was expected that demand and capacity would be balanced, and same-day appointments would be readily available for patients. The provider's would then be able to return to their regular hours.

The new templates were presented at a staff meeting. When staff members realized there would be added capacity and more open appointments, they were motivated and supported the new scheduling system.

Preparing for Implementation

Getting a handle on missed appointments was a critical factor in maximizing the schedule. The general lack of regard for scheduled appointments had to be addressed. Everyone (providers, staff and patients) needed to respect and honor scheduled appointments. This meant changing behavior and attitudes. This needed to happen to reduce the missed appointment rate before implementing the new scheduling system.

The manager and I prepared several pre-implementation in-services to overcome potential obstacles and reassure the staff. The first in-service covered the consequences of missed appointments and how the staff could help us lower the no-show rate by taking control of the schedule. Patients needed to view their appointments as a priority, and staff needed to send patients this message. Telephone scripts were prepared and used for role-playing. They included what to say and what not to say when confirming appointments or handling the no-show. We wanted to be sure the staff didn't send out subliminal messages giving patients permission to ignore an appointment or cancel at the last minute.

I took this opportunity to review the economic impact of no-shows and last-minute cancellations to help everyone understand how costly missed appointments are—not only financially, but also the disruption and loss of control that no-shows and double-booking causes. I assured the staff members that they had the power to reduce missed appointments and explained the benefits they would gain: manageable workflow, less disruption and predictable days. I provided the schedulers with the Appointment Power Words Matrix to guide them with booking, confirming appointments and handling patients with other scheduling issues. The message was clear— take control of the schedule to improve financial performance, manage patient flow, and improve patient compliance and continuity of care.

The clinical staff worked with the manager in developing tools to guide the schedulers in adapting to the new templates and open-access system. It was important for the schedulers to know what questions to ask patients to determine if they should schedule a quik-chek or standard appointment. The nurses developed cue cards with a list of probing questions for the schedulers to ask the patient. Together the staff participated in an interactive workshop, discussing various elements of the open-access system, how the patients were likely to respond, how the templates would work, the transition time frame and the importance of communicating and working together to fine-tune the process during the implementation.

The nurses agreed to provide additional assistance and further training for the schedulers during the adjustment period:

1. If the scheduler was unsure of what type of an appointment to schedule, the call was transferred to a nurse.
2. The nurses conducted weekly reviews with the schedulers. This provided an opportunity for open dialogue to further educate the schedulers, review the previous week's schedule and discuss problems that emerged and appointments that were questionable. This was a continuing education process that strengthened the schedulers' skills and confidence.

Managing the new templates effectively required optimizing the provider's time with patients. Nurses needed to do their part to have patients properly prepared for each visit. With the guidance of the manager, the providers and nurses developed a Rooming Matrix. It listed the reason for the visit, the chief complaints and the requirements needed to prepare a patient for the exam, based on the reason for the visit. For example, an annual physical would require checking weight, height, blood pressure, temperature, respirations and pulse. The nurse would also need to review medication, check allergies, obtain urine and blood samples and instruct the patient to completely undress and put on a full gown.

On the other hand, a patient with a dermatologic rash or mole would simply need to have his or her blood pressure and temperature taken, be questioned about allergies and be instructed to undress as required to expose the area. The nurse would also need to ask how long the patient had the condition and if it was painful or itched.

In order to make the most of the exam rooms and improve flow, patient instructions and education needed to take place elsewhere. A small storage room was converted into a patient education center. One of the nurses assumed responsibility for getting the center equipped with brochures and videos from pharmaceutical and equipment companies. Patient instructions, consent forms and other such materials were organized in files. This room became a vital factor in keeping the providers on schedule. When patients needed special instructions or materials at the conclusion of the visit, a nurse would take them to the center, complete the visit and answer their questions. This freed the exam room for the next patient and allowed the doctor or nurse practitioner to move on to the next patient.

The Implementation

The final step was placing the new templates in the computer system. Because the appointment calendar was booked until March 15, the target date for implementation was set for May 1. Patients scheduling beyond May 1 would be scheduled using the new template. In the meantime, the schedulers worked to reduce missed appointments. In mid-April, patients were sent an announcement of same-day scheduling availability. The providers also expanded their schedule by one hour beginning May 1. Weekly meetings were held to keep communication open and make any adjustments that might be required during the first 30 days.

Monitoring the Results

A patient satisfaction survey conducted before implementing the new scheduling system served as a baseline, followed by quarterly surveys the first year and annually thereafter.

Once the implementation process began, progress was closely observed. Everyone needed to stay on top of the schedule and take a critical look at what caused delays, taking steps to avoid a recurring pattern. Missed appointments were tracked, revealing a marked decrease in no shows and last minute cancellations. Follow-up time studies were conducted for three months straight to examine the progress being made with patient access and wait times.

The practice management reports tracked productivity—patient visits and charges for both the physician and the nurse practitioner—and payroll records revealed changes in overtime costs.

CHECKING OUT THE GAINS

The success of the revised appointment system was evident with the improvement in patient flow and access. Physician and staff efficiency skyrocketed. Tangible results at the six-month mark were proof that the practice had mastered the scheduling system:

- Patients were roomed within five minutes of arrival 93% of the time.
- Same-day access was available for established patients with the exception of annual exams.
- New-patient visits were scheduled within five days.
- Annual exams and pre-employment physicals were scheduled within seven days.
- No-shows and late cancellations were reduced by 70%.
- Patient satisfaction with obtaining appointments went from 25% to 87%.
- Overtime was under control, cutting payroll costs by more than $5,000/month.
- Revenue increased by 22%.
- Physicians and staff got out of the office on time more than 90% of the time.

The first six weeks were difficult, and the results were not evident for several months. During this time, some simple modifications to the original plan were required. The manager encountered a lack of confidence with some employees and minor resistance from one individual. A fair amount of reassurance and reinforcement was necessary before things stabilized. But in the end, everyone agreed it was well worth it!

THE SECRETS

1. There are classic symptoms of an unmanaged scheduling system.
2. Templates based on actual needs increase productivity and time management.
3. Missed appointments are costly to the practice.
4. Careful planning and staff involvement is essential to designing and implementing a realistic scheduling system.
5. An open access scheduling system improves patient service.
6. Educate staff and give them the tools they need.
7. To gain support for change, communicate the benefits.

FORMS ADDED TO YOUR TOOLBOX:

↪ *Appointment Power Words Matrix*
↪ *Rooming Matrix*

CHAPTER 6

Commonsense Risk Management

In my work as a consultant, physicians frequently express their concerns about potential malpractice litigation. This concern has been magnified in recent years—and with good cause. Malpractice suits are on the rise, and many of them are frivolous. The resulting increases in malprac-

KEY FACT: *There's more to risk management than clinical skills and clinical judgment.*

tice insurance premiums take a bigger bite out of doctors' income. It's no wonder physicians across the country are taking a defensive posture when it comes to medical decision-making and managing risk.

Managing risk is complex. There are, of course, clinical issues: the medical decision-making; the skill level of the physician and other care givers; and the outcome. Most risk-prevention strategies employed are related to physicians' clinical skills: physicians keep their clinical skills sharp and are diligent about continuing medical education in order to stay on top of emerging treatments for their specialty. The hospital's peer-review and quality-assurance programs help maintain standards of clinical care to further reduce risk.

But while physicians' clinical skills are vital in caring for their patients, managing risk and avoiding lawsuits, there's another side of risk management that seldom gets the attention it deserves. It's "commonsense" risk management, and it's not related to clinical skills or clinical judgment. It's a matter of how the office runs and how patients *feel* about their physician. These are important factors in keeping you out of court!

Commonsense risk management includes the relationship you have with patients, how well you communicate, the competency and training of your staff, your documentation procedures and the office systems you have in place to track and follow-up on patients. When you fail with these things, risk increases. It hardly matters what medical school you went to or if you are the best physician in town.

COULD IT HAPPEN TO YOU?

I am reminded of a practice I worked with a few years ago and a young physician that joined the practice the previous year. We'll call him Dr. Young. He graduated from an Ivy League school with honors and trained at a prestigious medical center. His diagnostic skills were amazing, and it didn't take long for him to get firmly rooted in the practice. He got along well with his colleagues and enjoyed both the practice and the patients. His partners were ecstatic to have him aboard.

Then one day, Dr. Young received a crushing blow and knew he would be faced with his first malpractice suit. Two months earlier, Mrs. Wilson had come to the office with chest pain and difficult, labored breathing. Dr. Young ordered a chest x-ray as part of his exam. Eight weeks later, Mrs. Wilson returned, because she wasn't getting better. When Dr. Young opened the chart and looked at his notes, he quickly flipped to the report on the chest x-ray. The report presented devastating news. Mrs. Wilson had lung cancer. Somehow, the report had been filed in the chart without the doctor ever seeing it. Because Mrs. Wilson didn't get a follow-up call from Dr. Young, she assumed the x-ray results presented no problems, and she continued following his treatment plan. When her symptoms increased and she started losing weight, she scheduled another appointment.

Dr. Young was not going to be sued because he was a mediocre physician or lacked clinical judgment, but because someone didn't follow office procedures. Something slipped through the cracks. Perhaps a new and improperly trained medical records person mistakenly filed the report. Maybe the procedures for handling reports were not well defined or perhaps they were inadequate. An office malfunction compromised this patient's care, not a lack of clinical expertise. Regardless, this oversight would be construed as medical negligence. Could this happen in your office?

Medical practice managers and physicians, take heed. It's important to look at the commonsense components of risk management and decide if your practice passes muster. It may be time to get your ship in order and develop an office-based risk management plan. Following are some key commonsense risk management strategies.

START WITH THE RELATIONSHIP

Developing a strong bond with your patients reduces the risk of malpractice suits. People are more than a little reluctant to sue their friends or people they really like, regardless of the nature of the suit.

It's not your job to become friends with your patients, but you do have an obligation to be friendly with your patients. Patients are judging you based on how personable you are and if you make them feel important. They are not equipped to judge your medical skills, and they wouldn't have scheduled an appointment with you unless they thought you were competent. Now it's up to you, beginning with the first impression. On the first visit, patients begin forming their opinion, and it's your job to win them over.

Consider the First Encounter

Begin by thinking about your first encounter with the patient. It is common for physicians to act as though the entire purpose of the visit is to get to the diagnosis and treat the problem. By all means, that is your clinical mission. But don't think that satisfying your clinical mission alone will result in satisfied patients that are grateful for the care they are given. When only clinical concerns are addressed, you are treating a condition and not the person. Patients, especially new patients, want and need more from you than clinical expertise. They want to feel important and believe that you care about them. If you get off to a bad start, it will be difficult to make up for it.

Most clinicians know the importance of good eye contact and a proper introduction, but that's only the start of your interaction with the patient. There are 10 golden rules that help physicians and mid-level providers build stronger patient relationships. Your medical office should integrate these rules into training manuals, and it's also important to periodically review these rules with your staff:

1. Once you are in the exam room, sit in a chair until you begin the examination. Looking down on patients makes them feel inferior. You want patients to feel and "know" that they are equal to you.
2. Read the chart before you go in the room. If the nurse wrote the reason for the visit in the chart there is no need for you to ask the patient why he or she is there.

3. Frequently refer to patients by name. It makes them feel you are connected and care about the whole person, not just their condition.
4. Get personal. It only takes a few minutes. Ask about the patient's hobbies, job or family. If you share an interest, so much the better.
5. Apologize if you're late, but don't act rushed. Your patients deserve your time. If you are relaxed and calm, they feel they have your attention and time.
6. Do not permit staff to interrupt you when you are with a patient unless absolutely necessary. Interruptions make patients feel like they're not a priority.
7. Do not use medical jargon the patient won't understand.
8. Never ask a patient a question unless you are willing to give your full attention to listen to the response. Look at the patient when either of you are speaking. Avoid looking at the chart while conversing, and don't interrupt.
9. Once you've presented your diagnosis, treatment and follow-up plan, do not assume the patient understands everything you said. Ask for affirmation and be willing to clarify or repeat your summation or instructions.
10. Before you complete each encounter, make sure that you have answered the patient's questions. Failure to completely answer questions results in unnecessary phone calls and frustrated patients.

Going the Extra Mile

A medical practice is not a commercial enterprise like the Ritz-Carlton, Nordstrom or Southwest Airlines, each known for taking pride in going the extra mile for its customers. Just the same, medical practices can benefit greatly by going the extra mile to build stronger relationships and make patients feel important. For example, when a patient has had an office-based operative procedure or has been in the hospital, why not call the patient the following day to see how he is doing? Ask if he has any questions and provide reassurance. If a patient who comes to the office appears to be too ill to be comfortable in the reception room, immediately escort her to an exam room so she can lie down. If patients have transportation problems, investigate what dial-a-ride services are available.

How we communicate goes a long way in making patients feel comfortable and cared about. The words we use can influence the patient experience. For example using the word "you" in some contexts makes people defensive—"Why did you do that?" The Communication Matrix added to the toolbox provides concrete examples that improve communication.

Think about having someone in the office assigned to be the patient advocate. A patient advocate provides special services for patients and makes sure their needs are met. An advocate also resolves complaints and smoothes out difficult situations—tempering a storm before it gets out of control. A patient advocate certainly gives the "we care" message and builds solid relationships with patients.

DOCUMENTATION

The written word tells the story. Physicians discover this when it's time to defend their records in court. It's not just getting things documented. It's a matter of legibility, timeliness and identifying who wrote what and when. Consult your legal advisor and medical liability insurance company to give you the specifics on what you should and shouldn't include in your documentation.

DEVELOP A RISK MANAGEMENT PLAN

The risk management related to documentation also includes handling and storage of records. Avoid a disaster similar to Dr. Young's. In my experience, fewer than 10% of medical practices have a written risk management plan. Generally, training on record keeping is ad hoc and sketchy at best, and nothing is in writing. Remember the old adage, if it isn't written down, it didn't happen. This applies not only to documenting your treatment, but to the risk management strategies the practice employs. The risk management plan and staff training on risk validate your commitment to managing risk.

Risk management plans usually include:
1. Record keeping
   a. Signature requirements
   b. Release of information
   c. Purging records
2. Samples of office forms related to medical record keeping
   a. Forms for HIPAA compliance
   b. Informed consent forms
   c. Medical records release

    d. Patient registration form and emergency contact release
3. Staff documentation policy and procedures
    a. Who documents what and who signs off
    b. Documentation time requirements (i.e., within the hour, at the end of session)
    c. Punitive action for noncompliance
    d. What reports require a signature
4. Documentation and record keeping
    a. Definition of performance standards
    b. Performance measurement
    c. Quality assurance/peer review
5. Staff medical records training modules
    a. Clinicians
    b. Medical records staff
    c. Billing staff
    d. Front office
6. Tracking system and procedures
    a. Diagnostic studies ordered in office or elsewhere
    b. Reporting methods
    c. Recall system
    d. Missed appointments
7. Medical records audit procedures
    a. Coding and documentation
    b. Risk management
8. Discharging the noncomplaint patient
    a. Protocol
    b. Sample discharge letter

Some components of this risk management plan are specific to the practice, and others are part of most medical practices' office procedures. For example, the release of medical records and signature requirements may be clear to your staff members, but they aren't written in a formal plan. Your practice likely has a series of form letters, such as those relating to HIPAA; informed consent forms; and other forms important to record keeping for patients, and these forms may not exist in one master manual. Your challenge is to set standards, define punitive actions and develop medical record training modules. When preparing a risk management plan, practices often discover their tracking and recall systems could use fine-tuning.

Setting Standards

Setting standards with documentation and record keeping begins with physicians respecting the medical chart. If they don't respect it, how can they expect the staff to do so? Staff members of one practice told me they couldn't find records that were in the trunk of a doctor's car because he took a stack home over the weekend to get caught up on "last week's" dictation.

In the future, the use of electronic health records (EHRs) will improve our ability to standardize office practices, improving documentation and accountability. In the meantime, it is still important to address these issues.

Begin setting performance standards by focusing on that which most directly influences the patient's safety and medical care, as well as that which might be construed as negligence on the practice's part. Start with the top priority items and create a list. Here are a few examples, but each practice should prepare a list of standards based on its standard protocol. If standard protocols are not in place, develop them now.

Rooming a patient: What specific items is the nurse/medical assistant to document when rooming a patient? Naturally, this will vary by specialty and type of appointment, but may include: date; vital signs, temperature and weight; presenting symptoms and duration; medications; and initialing the documentation.

Responding to patient phone calls (clinical): What documentation and actions are required for handling incoming clinical telephone calls? Is it a double-entry system or a duplicate system with the original placed in the chart? Are the date and time of call, primary and secondary phone numbers, symptoms and temperature recorded? Are the initials of the person who took the message recorded? Who is the information routed to and how is it routed? When is the call considered emergent and routed to a nurse/doctor? What should the caller be told about when to expect a reply? (This should be consistent and reliable.) What is the maximum time before the call is returned?

Documenting the visit: What are your requirements for physicians and mid-level providers regarding documentation—scribes, dictation, handheld or by hand? What are your legibility and signature requirements? Do you have dictation sign-off requirements (i.e., date dictated, date transcribed)? Do you have time limits for dictation, transcription, typed/signed and in the chart? What are your rules on physician chart handling, the need for charts to remain on the premises and when a chart must be released to return to files? Define limits for holding on to charts.

Patient's rights and confidentiality: What is the practice's responsibility and what are the patient's rights with respect to their medical record, specifically access to information, release of information and costs for duplication?

Use these few examples as a starting point for meeting with physicians and staff to agree on documentation requirements and responsibilities. Once you have finalized the measurements, set the standard. For example, are phone calls to be transferred immediately when they seem emergent or should they be written up and routed to the nurse for action within 10 minutes? Are other clinical calls to be returned within one to two hours? Is dictation to be completed by the end of the session and in the chart within 24 hours? Make decisions and set policy!

Punitive Measures

When the standards are formalized and become part of the risk management plan, establish a method to monitor compliance. Will you pull random charts and have a monthly or bi-monthly audit to check dictation or legibility of the provider and whether entries are initialed? Will you use the duplicate telephone log to pull random phone calls to see how they were handled? Beyond this, the plan needs to outline punitive measures as well as define when punitive actions are appropriate—on the first occurrence, the third or the tenth? This can be a political tightrope, but these components are essential in an effective plan. The four key elements to developing the standards are:
1. Identifying the standards;
2. Determining the measurement;
3. Developing a method to monitor compliance; and
4. Creating accountability with well-defined punitive actions.

Staff Training Guides

Developing staff training guides is easier once you have developed standards. The standards become the blueprint to help you develop training guides for each department. In addition to using the training guides for medical records and documentation as part of your risk management program, your plan should also include training on communication and customer service. Each staff member must understand his or her role in building and maintaining strong relationships with patients.

Tracking Systems

Tracking systems are important to ensure that follow-up studies and exams are ordered and completed. It's also important for ensuring that you obtain results for biopsies and lab work you send out of the office.

Some of the tracking in the medical office can be done with the computer, and, fortunately, most practices have a computerized practice management system. These systems usually include an appointment-scheduling module with a recall system that can automatically send patients reminders. Most systems also have the capability to pull reports for specific conditions that need follow-up. With an EHR, you have even greater tracking capabilities. Computerized systems are the most reliable tracking systems. But remember, you have to put the information in to be able to sort the data and get the reports you need. The reliability of *any system* still depends on the people using it.

Many practices have a computer system for billing, but fail to explore its tracking capabilities. If you have a computer and you aren't using it for recall and tracking missed appointments, it's time to meet with your vendor and explore the system's tracking tools. If your system is limited, there are products on the market that can be integrated with existing computer systems to automate patient reminders and appointment confirmation. It's certainly worth exploring your options.

Other tracking systems are manual. For diagnostic studies that are ordered, a manual log is easy to implement and does a good job of tracking. Create a log with columns to write the patient's name, date, tests ordered, what facility is performing the study and the date the report is received. The reliability of such a system depends on staff documenting in real-time. As soon as the order is given, log it in; as soon as the report is received, log it in. Monitor the log, and when reports are not received within the standard time, place a call and get them faxed over immediately. Once the report is logged in, follow proper procedures to see that it is read and initialed by the doctor and that the patient has been informed. These procedures should be written in your risk management plan.

A "tickler" file is another typical manual system that consists of an index card on each patient that is being tracked for a specific purpose. Key information will be documented on the card, including the follow-up date. The index cards are then kept in a master card box by month/week for follow-up. This is a common practice for following up on breast exams, mammograms, Pap smears and other rechecks. An accordion file system is sometimes used in a similar way, keeping the order sheet for follow-up studies in a tickler file by month.

Many practices have electronic messaging or "telephone in" service. This gives the patient access to test results. When tests are ordered, the patient is given a card with a phone number to access the system and a time frame to call for the test results. Once the test results are received, the doctor notes the findings and makes comments on the report. The nurse then records a message in the system for the patient to hear. There are obvious benefits to electronic reporting of results: it is more productive for the office than mailing, gives the patient control and is confidential.

When it comes to tracking, computer systems have come a long way, and there are many products that work with existing practice management systems. If you are not fully automated, now would be a good time to advance your use of technology. Consider these technologies as an opportunity to strengthen your risk management efforts, increase patient compliance and improve clinical outcomes.

In any tracking system, staff members need to understand the importance of the system and how to use and manage it. If an office system fails, one of the first questions a plaintiff's attorney will ask will relate to the adequacy of employee orientation. The training guide and risk management plan you develop will be your defense.

DISCHARGING PATIENTS

It's difficult to make a decision to discharge a patient. It's a very big decision, like firing an employee. Most physicians and managers avoid it until they see no alternative. But, just like terminating an employee, if it isn't dealt with when the signs first become evident, you may regret it later. A noncompliant patient represents a risk to the practice. So does the patient that is antagonistic to the point where the physician-patient relationship deteriorates. The most common reasons for discharging a patient are:
- Noncompliance related to medical treatment;
- Abrasive, abusive or threatening behavior; and
- Noncompliance with payment for services.

Regardless of the reason, when the practice determines it is time to sever the relationship, it is important to proceed with cautious, but decisive actions.

Physicians are obligated to continue treating a patient until the patient's condition no longer warrants treatment or the patient discharges the physician. When the physician terminates the relationship, it is important to take specific steps that ensure the patient is not abandoned:

- Do not withdraw from caring for a patient in the midst of a medical crisis.
- Verbally discharge the patient in person.
- Confirm the discharge in a letter signed by the physician.
- Establish a date for termination, depending on the patient's condition and availability of a qualified physician to take over the patient's care; usually this is somewhere between 2 weeks and 30 days.
- Describe the patient's current condition.
- Inform the patient of the need to select another physician.
- Indicate whether follow-up care should be immediate.
- Indicate prognosis if follow-up care is not obtained.
- Inform the patient of other physicians qualified to provide care.
- Let the patient know you are available for emergencies or to treat acute conditions in the interim.
- Inform the patient that the practice will provide copies of his or her medical record to the patient's new physician upon receiving written authorization and that you are available to consult with the new physician if requested.
- Send the letter by certified mail, return receipt requested.
- File the mail receipt in the patient's chart once it is received.
- Inform the staff not to schedule another appointment once the transition time has ended and follow up by flagging the patient's account in the computer system.

I offer a word of caution in handling the noncompliant patient when it involves payment for services. Once an account is considered noncollectible, do not allow staff to turn the account over to a collection agency until the physician has reviewed the chart. This allows the doctor to determine if, based on the patient relationship or medical condition, such actions would aggravate the patient in a way that might pose the threat of a malpractice suit.

TAPPING INTO RISK MANAGEMENT RESOURCES

Managers and physicians need to build a strong alliance with their malpractice insurance carriers. You share the same goal: avoiding a malpractice lawsuit. Ask your carrier if it will conduct a risk prevention audit and what risk prevention tools it can provide for the office. Carriers will usually offer you additional assistance in determining what types of continuing education on risk management are available to you.

ATTITUDES

Risk management is a silent duty. Unfortunately, the silence sometimes doesn't get the practice's attention until a problem emerges. It's far better to take a proactive posture to avoid problems. Yes, developing a risk management plan requires time and effort. Because of this, physicians and staff may view such a project as a pain or nuisance, or may put it on the back burner until it's too late. Don't place yourself in that position. Physicians and managers that initiate and endorse the development of a risk management plan will be glad they made the effort. Make commonsense risk management a priority!

THE SECRETS

1. Focus on the patient relationship from the first visit.
2. Patients form their opinion about their doctors based on people skills, not clinical skills.
3. The entire practice plays a role in risk prevention.
4. Employ commonsense risk management strategies.
5. Document clinical activities in real-time.
6. There are specific requirements to properly discharge a patient.
7. Establish standards and measurements for medical record keeping.
8. Turn to your malpractice insurance carrier for guidance and support.
9. A risk management plan is vital to protecting your practice.

> ### FORMS ADDED TO YOUR TOOLBOX:
> ◌ *Communication Matrix*
> ◌ *Tracking Log for Diagnostic Studies*
> ◌ *Sample Discharge Letter*

CHAPTER 7

Shredding the Paper Monster

Electronic health records (EHRs; also referred to as "electronic medical records") are touted as a solution to inefficiency and a means of reducing paperwork in the medical practice. As the federal government continues to push EHRs, it certainly is getting the attention of many medical practices. However, EHRs still seem to be something a number of physicians love to hate. They don't even want to think about selecting and purchasing an EHR system, let alone going through the time-consuming and ominous implementation process.

> **KEY FACT:** *Proper planning for and the successful implementation of an electronic health records system require a commitment that starts with the physicians and is reinforced by management.*

These reluctant physicians see EHRs as a costly investment and/or have heard horror stories about *what went wrong*—and they don't want to get involved. This is understandable. But it is quickly becoming essential for physicians to establish a target date to convert to EHRs, plan for the time requirements to select and implement the best system, and to be prepared for the financial and emotional investment essential to making this transition.

The financial cost and time involved to purchase the system and the time and cost required to transition to an EHR system are not minor challenges for busy medical practices that are concerned about shrinking reimbursements while operating costs keep going up. However, in the face of government pressure that aims to incentivize physicians for *meaningful* implementation of an EHR system and eventually penalize those that don't, it's time to start evaluating your needs and planning for the future. This means exploring the opportunities and advantages EHR systems offer and what it might mean to your practice's future.

WHERE DO YOU START?

The answer to that question depends on you. If you are a new doctor getting ready to open a practice, your life will be a lot easier if you begin your practice by implementing both a practice management system (PMS) and EHRs to optimize efficiency from the get-go. For the rest of you, selecting and implementing an EHR system is a very involved process.

It often starts with one of the physicians or the manager recognizing the need and bringing it to the attention of the practice's leadership. The impetus for this could be that the practice has outgrown its current PMS or it is simply out of date. It could be a physician that has a strong desire to capture data to measure and improve outcomes. For others, it could be the availability of stimulus funds from the federal government. It could even be the lure of a great system that seems affordable. The motivation could be simply hearing about someone else's success story.

Whatever the motivation, there are practical and technical issues that need to guide the selection process, including HIPAA requirements. Data-sharing and interfacing are needed, as is consideration for whether physicians will be using PDAs to access and input information off-site.

Obtaining this information is critical to adequately examining different systems and evaluating potential solutions. The practice should list each item and rate it with a weighted scale based on priority as follows:

4. Critical requirement
3. Important requirement
2. Nice to have
1. Optional requirement

Rating the ability of a product to meet a specific need helps you quantify the capabilities, strengths and weaknesses of a product instead of relying on everyone's memory. Ideally, these ratings should be recorded during the demonstration by all participants.

For those of you with reservations about selecting and integrating an EHR system, there may be a light at the end of the tunnel. Following is a case study of a busy group pediatric practice that converted to EHRs. When it began looking at systems in 2005, the practice had 12 physicians. If they can succeed, so can you!

MAKING AN EHR SYSTEM A PRIORITY

Pediatric Associates of Richmond (PAR) in Richmond, Virginia, knows the challenges of selecting and integrating an EHR system. "We were in the dark ages of technology," the office manager, Josephine "Jo" DiPerna, said. PAR's UNIX-based PMS was out of date and couldn't possibly meet the technology needs of the future. The need to upgrade became apparent a few years back, and it seemed logical to get a system that included EHRs.

At that time, the billing department and the schedulers were the only ones that had experience with technology application in the medical practice, and the system they had was antiquated.

Although they were talking about moving in the direction of technology, the impetus to get started really took off in 2005, when one of the physicians returned from a conference where a sales rep pitched a practice management and EHR system and convinced the doctor that the practice could be up and running on the new system within six weeks.

According to the sales rep, this product could do just about everything but turn out the lights. PAR would soon learn how unrealistic this was—especially for a practice with 12 physicians.

In the Beginning

This story began when the physician returned from that conference in 2005 and touted the value of the system he saw. This was the trigger for the manager to look not only at that system, but other systems to compare and determine the best fit. She recruited a team to help her through this process: Nicole Midulla, the front office supervisor; Matthew Andrako, PAR's troubleshooter, who has since become the practice's information technology (IT) specialist; and the billing manager who has since left the practice and was replaced by Lisa Kirby, who came on board the following year.

It was easy for the team to be impressed because they were looking at easy-to-use Windows-based systems that were far superior to the antiquated system they were using. The team didn't realize what questions they should be asking in order to compare and fully understand all the systems. Each product seemed perfect. They were buying the glitz.

There was one exception—the billing manager. Based on her knowledge and the fact that she had lived through a conversion with another practice, she asked pointed questions about each system's capabilities and performance during the demos, revealing some of the systems' flaws. Her questions alerted the rest of the team members to their own need for greater system knowledge before they could make a prudent decision.

How could they possibly select the best system for the practice, let alone plan for a successful implementation? This purchase would be a costly investment, and the implementation for a practice this size would be a major project. They needed help.

Turning to Experts

The investment made in hiring a healthcare management information specialist is well worth the cost. It allows a practice to avoid pitfalls other practices have encountered. Converting a PMS, learning a new system and bringing EHRs on board is an enormous undertaking. The guidance of an expert will make a huge difference in keeping the practice on track and achieving the desired results.

However, selecting the right advisor is a challenge of its own. PAR talked to a local company that spent half a day interviewing the search team in order to prepare a proposal to present to the core decision-making physicians. When the same company reps returned for the scheduled meeting, the reps were totally unprepared. There was no proposal, and they were asking the same questions they asked before. "It was a total waste of time and a frustrating experience," declared Jo.

One day in the midst of the chaos, Jo read an article by Ron Sterling, C.P.A., M.B.A., President of Sterling Solutions, Ltd., and was impressed by what he had to say. Ron helps healthcare organizations capitalize on technology to improve patient service, clinical operations and financial results. Jo interviewed Ron on the telephone and discussed the practice's situation. She then set up an appointment for him to meet the selection team. During that meeting, the team members shared their demo experiences, their goals and their concerns about making the right decision and how overwhelming the project had become.

While talking with Ron, they quickly learned about the potential errors they could have made. None of the systems they had looked at were sophisticated enough or had the capacity to meet the needs of a practice their size. Without Ron, they would not have realized this and might have made a costly mistake.

The Commitment

Ron made it clear that the first step was to meet with the physicians and give them an understanding of what would be involved and required to move PAR into the age of technology and implement a new system that would meet their goals and provide for future growth. He was brutally honest about what it takes to succeed with EHRs.

Ron met with the Board, which is composed of all the physicians. He told them this would cost a lot of money, they could expect it to be painful and there would be times when they were likely to actually hate the system that eventually they would learn to love. But the most important thing he told them was that if they didn't buy into this as a group, they would be wasting time and money and could not succeed. There could be no passive-aggressive holdouts. He certainly got the Board's attention. "He was truthful and right on," said Jo. The Board agreed that they needed Ron to guide them through a successful transition and took his advice.

Ron explained that running everything by the 12-physician board would not be feasible, so a committee of three physicians was appointed to work with the selection team. This group of seven worked with Ron through the selection, planning and implementation.

Planning

The planning process actually starts long before a vendor selection is made. It's a matter of going through the many steps necessary to make a proper selection and implementing the system efficiently. It requires project management at both a practical and complex level. This team was ready for the challenge.

Getting Ready

Ron advised hiring a local company for IT installation and support, which has been invaluable. Early on, Ron suggested that Matthew was overqualified for his current responsibilities and would be a good fit to become the internal IT liaison for Pediatric Associates. With this in mind, Matthew took on additional responsibilities during the planning and integration to the new system and was trained to coordinate the in-house IT functions and work with the outside IT company long term. This has been an invaluable role in troubleshooting system problems.

It was important for PAR to understand what specific issues and features were needed in a system in order to clearly identify the system requirements, including:

- Support;
- Documentation;
- Upgrades;
- Back-up options;

- Security; and
- Practice structure and function.

Because of the size of the practice and its data needs, the system installation for PAR required a dedicated room with particular specifications, such as temperature control.

The Decision

It took a number of months for the practice team to examine different systems, analyze the options and select the software product even though Ron did much of the upfront research. He provided the team with a shortlist of viable systems to examine and worksheets to help with this part of the project.

Pediatric Associates selected Pulse Systems and signed contracts for both software and hardware within a three-month period. Thanks to Ron, the contract with Pulse included a clause that required the company to provide PAR with up to 35 individual templates to the EHR system. This was very important to the physicians and mid-level providers of this practice that consisted of 12 physicians with 4 nurse practitioners, and had appointment scheduling that included extended hours during the week and weekends. The customized templates would aid the practice in adapting to electronic documentation that was specific to the treatments the practice provided and its past documentation patterns.

Behind the Scenes

Once a decision was made and the contracts were signed, the facility needed to prepare to accommodate the equipment and complete the installation. This took the better part of the first few months and kept Matthew very busy. It required substantial direction and support from the hardware experts as well. The hardware installation took place in the summer of 2006. At the same time, the team needed to examine workflow solutions and plan for both the PMS data conversion and implementation of the EHRs.

It is important to understand what data support is needed from the old system once the PMS conversion takes place. Each vendor works differently, and the practice needs to review its existing maintenance contracts and plan for support needs during the interim and until the old system is no longer needed. Ron was instrumental in accomplishing this for Pediatric Associates.

Ron prepared a timeline, which was critical to the ability to accomplish a smooth transition for PAR. The timeline detailed key actions and listed critical path issues that needed to be dealt with. It is important to recognize that the timeline for a conversion and integration to new software and hardware is a living document that requires revisions when critical decision points or actions cause a delay in meeting other deadlines.

Workflow

Early on, the project team worked with staff and physicians to get an understanding of how the workflow was accomplished with a manual system and how that workflow would change when the new EHR system was implemented. This required a great deal of cooperation; the team had to be a champion for change and help staff members get a sense of the gains they would achieve with the new technology that was so unfamiliar.

Patient Registration

The practice wanted clean demographic information on its patients. This required collecting a new patient registration on each patient. It was expected that managing this during patient hours would create a backlog. So to minimize the effects of this, management planned to increase staffing during the first few months of going live on the new PMS. To help ease the pain, some of the "frequent flyers," those patients that were in the office frequently, were entered into the system in advance. Some patient registrations were entered during the practice training sessions, but for the most part, other patients would be registered instead at their first appointment following implementation.

Medical Records

Maintaining data from the paper charting system presented a challenge because Pediatric Associates had family charts. Nicole had the presence of mind to recognize this could become a major problem if not handled in advance. The practice began separating clinic records by individual patient a year in advance. This reduced the scanning burden considerably and helped manage the workflow when it came time to implement the EHR system.

Clinical Flow

The clinical flow issues would emerge once the practice was preparing for EHR implementation, scheduled to take place about a year after the PMS conversion.

To help ease the transition to EHRs, a physician team was selected to work on the clinical care templates in advance. Two somewhat reluctant physicians were appointed. This served to obtain their buy-in and keep them more involved—a smart strategy for other practices to consider.

Documenting and billing for hospital care was not a major concern for PAR because hospitalists manage patient care for those that are admitted to the hospital. The only hospital care provided by Pediatric Associates is the newborn examinations. These are scheduled in advance and did not pose a problem for adapting EHRs.

One of the bigger challenges would be managing time in the clinic for nurses and physicians that were unfamiliar with EHRs and the time needed to adjust to documenting on an electronic chart. "This is not an open-the-box, plug-and-play system," said Matthew. Both physicians and staff needed to understand this and be committed to the time and training required.

Training

User training on the PMS began at the end of September 2006. There was initially some resistance from members of the billing department: they were comfortable with the antiquated system and thought too many steps were required in using a Windows-based program. To top it off, they were not accustomed to using a mouse. Fortunately, over time they learned to appreciate the system, its capabilities, its reliability and the time it saves. The practice was fully transitioned to the new PMS before the practice converted to EHRs.

Physician training was an essential component of getting prepared to implement the EHRs. It can be a challenge to get physicians to understand and become proficient at documenting electronically. The training was intensive and took place in the spring of 2007.

Most of the staff became enthused about the project and worked hard to get the practice through the change. So did the physicians. Evening training classes meant long hours and sometimes endless days during both the training and the transition.

There were challenges with clinical support staff, since the practice's organizational chart did not have a nurse leadership position to guide the process of evaluating workflows and preparing for the EHR conversion. The nursing staff had little knowledge of technology and did not want to take responsibility to evaluate workflow for the EHR conversion or to put in the extra hours to accomplish it. This placed additional responsibility on Nicole and Matthew to gain an understanding of clinical flow and charting needs, and to provide training and support for clinical staff.

Implementation

Pediatric Associates elected to implement the PMS first because the billing department and schedulers were already using technology and the existing system was so antiquated. Implementation for a practice of this size is not easy; it's a tedious process that can be frustrating and requires a lot of teamwork.

PAR's success with implementation is apparent by the fact that it did not shut down the schedule during conversion. "We did not lose one day of production, and the conversion (both PMS and EHR) was seamless to the patients," stated Jo. This was a remarkable feat.

Master files were set up on the PMS, and the data conversion, which was limited to patient names and account numbers, took place from mid-August through late September 2006.

Electronic PMS data conversion included a test conversion at the end of August 2006 and a final live conversion at the end of September 2006. Due to the limitations of the old PMS, PAR staff had to put in a significant amount of time manually entering information that could not be converted from the old system or new information that was never in the old PMS.

Although some patients were registered in advance, most patients completed a patient information form at the time of the first post-conversion visit, and the data were then entered into the Pulse System. It was impossible to stay completely current on this in the beginning, and it required additional staffing hours. Since this was determined prior to implementation, staff was prepared to be assigned this task and work longer hours to control the workflow during the transition. The backlog was whittled down during the first few months.

Management made every effort to show its appreciation and encourage staff by maintaining a spirit of cooperation and support. For example, during the periods when they were scanning, backloading and pre-scheduling, staff members were provided with pizza and donuts to keep them going. "We celebrated our successes when different benchmarks were achieved during the project," said Jo. This kept the staff motivated and feeling a sense of appreciation for what they had accomplished.

Patient appointments were entered into the new system manually at the end of September in preparation for the conversion and "go-live" on the new PMS, which took place in mid-October—less than three months from when the contracts were signed. "We went from crayons to computers in one fell swoop," stated the manager when referring to the new PMS.

The accounts receivable remained on the old system until it was collected. This was the best approach to ensuring information entered onto the new system would be accurate.

Next Stop: EHRs

The planning team looked at the local hospital's scanning process and quickly realized they needed to scan both sides of the record so no one could claim data were missing. They started prepping the charts for electronic conversion a year ahead of time. Organizing the charts and understanding what must be scanned, where the information would be located in the EHR and where the original paper chart was stored was a complex process.

Prior to implementing the EHR, each patient record needed to be scanned. This was critical. It was doable because the practice was prepared and because the go-live was limited to two physicians at a time. An entire crew was hired to do a final chart prep (a tedious and time-consuming process) to be ready for scanning and to scan the documents when the practice rolled out the EHRs. People don't realize how much time it takes to sort through a patient chart; remove staples and paper clips; and tape loose papers, small notes and lab reports to prepare documents for scanning. It took this additional staff three months to scan the necessary patient information into the electronic chart.

Bringing two physicians on to the EHR system every two or three weeks helped manage the support and workflow needs. Not every encounter was documented in real-time. This accomplishment varies among physicians, based on their own practice style and workflow patterns.

During the early implementation, these physicians would not leave the office for several hours after the last appointment of the day in order to get their charting complete. Speed only comes with time and acclimation.

A Success Story

Pediatric Associates is a success story. This is a testimony of the practice's commitment to shredding the paper monster and embracing technology to improve performance.

This practice was thoughtful and deliberate in its approach to implementing a new PMS and EHR system. It dedicated the time to plan, prepare and execute under the guidance of a skilled consultant. A timeline was developed and used to monitor progress, approach milestones and meet deadlines.

The team members worked well together and managed to get the advance commitment of physicians and staff, and continued to work with a common mission to achieve a high level of integration without compromising patient service or placing unreasonable demands on physicians or staff. "It can be hard to learn a new system. You need to be positive and have a *can do* attitude," advised Nicole. "And it takes patience."

Most importantly, the commitment of physicians was solid. Ron stated, "The decision to adopt [an EHR system] was not easy, but was backed by the process and empowered by the physicians." This aspect of Pediatric Associates is a significant factor to its success as a practice and with EHR integration.

Biggest Challenges

Like any practice going through this conversion, PAR faced challenges along the way:

1. The benefits of going paperless were not recognized immediately. It took time to become completely functional in this environment and achieve the economies and rewards.
2. Because PAR's existing technology was so antiquated, it needed to completely replace existing software and hardware.
3. Converting from family charts to individual patient charts was a time-consuming process for such a big and busy practice.
4. Pediatric practices need to track and report on immunizations. This required backloading immunization data. The entry of immunization data was further complicated by some clinical decision-making and analysis that required the skills and support of a nursing staff that was unfamiliar with technology and had very little understanding of the gains it offered. Due to availability and some logistics, the backloading of immunization information was stockpiled at times.
5. The transition of documenting directly into the EHR system at the time of the patient visit is the most challenging part of an EHR-adoption process, and PAR was no exception. Some of the physicians have not

fully adjusted. It requires a sustained effort and continued support to help doctors and staff rise to the next level of use and begin implementing sophisticated methods of measuring outcomes and developing best-practice performance in both administrative and clinical functions.

The Pay Off

The new system integrating PMS and EHR was a welcome addition to this practice. The practice is now tech-savvy and prepared for the future. It is working more efficiently, and workflow is vastly improved.

Through attrition PAR has been able to reduce staffing by 1.5 people in the billing department and 2.5 in front office support.

The new PMS has:
1. Fewer steps;
2. Increased capabilities to better manage the revenue cycle;
3. Faster, more sophisticated reporting; and
4. Scheduling templates that are more user-friendly.

The new EHR system has the following benefits:
1. No paper charts means as many as 20 hours a week saved from maintaining a paper system, including retrieving, filing and finding missing charts.
2. Laboratory results and reports from other physicians are scanned into the EHR often within 24 hours of receipt, eliminating a prior backlog of 30 days and endless time searching for information.
3. Chart documentation takes place in real-time.
4. Nurses don't have to search for a chart to answer a patient's phone call, saving time and improving response time.
5. The on-call physician has immediate access to up-to-date patient records.
6. Prescriptions can be faxed or e-mailed at time of entry.
7. There is the ability to interface orders and reports internally and with outside laboratories.

LESSONS LEARNED

It is important to be cautious when selecting the most appropriate vendor for both medical practice management and EHR software. You must have a clear understanding of your needs and whether the selected vendors are capable of meeting those needs.

Shifting to an EHR system requires cautious planning and the guidance of experts in the field. Larger practices may have such expertise within their organization, but it is too much to expect the management of a medical group with fewer than 20 physicians to handle such a major undertaking without gaining more knowledge and expertise on what is involved. Ron Sterling's book *Keys to EMR/EHR Success, 2nd Edition* (Greenbranch Publishing, 2010) is a good first step to understanding the process.

Expect the progression from onset to complete transformation to take a considerable amount of time, and understand that physician support is essential to the project's success. Also, remember physicians need a fair amount of training and time to learn a new system for documenting encounters and to transition to doing so in real-time.

Finally, although you may have a search committee, it is vitally important to get input from everyone that will be using the new system and to clearly understand workflow processes that will change with the implementation of new technology. After all, these changes are for the greater good.

THE SECRETS

1. Know what you don't know and when to call in the experts.
2. Physician and leadership commitment is essential to success.
3. Consider everyone's needs and concerns, and address them to get their support.
4. Dedicate time to planning.
5. Celebrate your planning and implementation successes incrementally.
6. Understand existing workflow needs and how they will change with a conversion to EHRs.
7. Recognize the technology IQ of staff, and provide essential training to increase their confidence and capabilities to use the new system before you go live.
8. The gains are worth the challenges, time commitment and cost of converting to EHRs.
9. EHRs will reduce processes, decrease errors and improve consistency.

FORM ADDED TO YOUR TOOLBOX:
☞ *Sample EHR Project Timeline Schematic*

CHAPTER 8

The Changing Dynamics of Outpatient Academic Practices

S ome of our nation's best physicians are affiliated with prestigious academic medical centers. They are conducting important research that will change the face of medicine, teaching a future generation of physicians and treating patients with rare and complicated illnesses. These physicians are vital to the practice of medicine and the future health of the world. We need them, we admire them and we find them a challenge.

> **KEY FACT:** *Performance expectations that impact the faculty practice culture must not compromise the institution's traditional academic values.*

This chapter represents a composite of outpatient clinics for different faculty practices I've worked with during my career, gathering bits of wisdom, sharing concepts, overcoming obstacles and discovering the secrets to success.

COMPETING PRIORITIES

The divergent interests and responsibilities of the academic physician result in both challenges and opportunities. These physicians are considered the cream of the crop. They are the best of the best and are sought after for their talents. They must spread their talents among four competing priorities: research, teaching, clinical patient care and administration.

A WORLD OF DIFFERENCE

In the world of medicine, the faculty practice functions differently than the private practice. Faculty practices are typically situated on large campuses in the inner city. Patients come from far and wide, and they willingly deal with the traffic, parking problems and confusion of finding the clinic. They want to see the all-knowing physician they've heard so much about. They are hoping for a treatment that will give them back a normal life. These patients are often competing for too few appointments, an unfortunate reality.

These exceptional academic physicians, unlike many physicians in private practice, don't have four days a week to devote to the outpatient clinic. Their research, teaching and administrative responsibilities can be all consuming. These divergent interests conflict with the need to accommodate clinic patients and be financially self-sustaining. Academic physicians are not accustomed to running the practice like a business, and it is not something they want to deal with. By contrast, private practice physicians understand their survival depends on turning a profit.

ADMINISTRATIVE CHALLENGES

Traditionally, the greatest source of job satisfaction for academic physicians is the recognition for academic accomplishments. Faculty physicians are absorbed in their pursuit of academic endeavors: conducting extensive research projects that will advance medicine and teaching the physicians of tomorrow. Their clinic interests and responsibilities often take a secondary position.

Typically, the academic culture focuses on the research and teaching responsibilities of faculty and does not seriously reward outpatient clinical performance. Administration must employ methods that honor and reward physicians for their clinical performance. Realistic expectations must be established and enforced. This may not be popular with academic physicians, but it is essential to the faculty practice's ability to become a self-sustaining entity, much like its peers in private practice.

Compensation plans that pay physicians based on their performance/contribution to direct patient care create an incentive for the academic physician to more fully participate. If the income distribution does not pay for performance, academic physicians will not be inclined to change their attitudes about increased participation in clinical services. The pay-for-performance compensation model is a business approach to running the outpatient clinic. This change in culture for the faculty practice must be approached in a way that does not compromise the institution's traditional academic values.

Centralization

The business side of academic medicine has moved to the forefront with the appearance of managed care and reduced reimbursement. Major teaching hospitals have developed centralized administrative organizations to address the business and economic needs of the academic faculty practice. These organizations have a variety of names and associated acronyms such as: management service organization (MSO), centralized business office (CBO) and management business office (MBO). Their primary purpose is to assume responsibility for administrative services to increase operational efficiency and improve financial performance of the faculty practice.

When business functions are provided by centralized services, administration monitors and reports on the performance of the outpatient clinic, something the physicians are not accustomed to. If finances are scrutinized and productivity expectations emerge, physicians resist, making it difficult to obtain the cooperation essential to improving productivity, efficiency and finances.

The implementation of centralized administrative services generally begins with assuming responsibility for managing clinic revenue and expenses, including the billing and collections processes. Once this is successful, other functions are delegated to centralized administration, such as handling incoming phone calls, scheduling and staffing the clinic. Physicians may resist these changes for fear more expectations will be put upon them, a potential threat to their academic interests.

Physicians must be convinced that centralizing clinic functions offers substantial benefits to them and will not add burdens to already-demanding work schedules. This can be accomplished if the physicians share management's objectives, and they work together to achieve them. The physicians must believe that there is a valid need to move the clinic in a new direction, their interests are protected and the gains are worth the effort. This requires an evaluation of the outpatient clinic's performance.

The clinic assessment provides detailed objective findings that are data-driven and compared with a valid benchmark. This is best achieved by selecting someone outside the organization to conduct the study. An independent consulting team has no political agenda or bias to cloud its opinions. When sound analysis and recommendations are presented, academic physicians are less resistant. If administration is willing to be measured by the same yardstick, this becomes even more convincing. The performance report card then becomes the physicians' baseline to compare the administrations' future performance when centralized services are implemented.

OPERATIONAL ASSESSMENT

The success of the operational assessment requires a clear understanding of the organizational culture, structure, leadership, communication and decision-making processes. The project objectives and related concerns must be clearly defined and agreed upon. The final report is expected to provide recommendations that support any or all of these organizational objectives:

1. Strengthen communication;
2. Develop shared objectives;
3. Improve operating performance;
4. Standardize patient services;
5. Increase patient satisfaction;
6. Improve financial performance; and
7. Attain self-sustaining financial position.

   The influence and value of the report are directly related to a clear rationale for each recommendation and identifying the associated risks, opportunities and economic impact. A Risk/Opportunity Matrix is an effective visual tool to assist in accomplishing this. If the argument for change is not compelling, it will be difficult to obtain the desired commitment.

CLINIC PERFORMANCE

Conducting an analysis of the faculty practice is an arduous process that includes:

- Collecting relevant documents and historical data;
- Preparing and distributing survey instruments;
- Conducting interviews;
- Examining comparative secondary data;
- Performing the on-site review; and
- Developing and presenting the report.

   The assessment focuses on the typical operational systems involved with patient services—from the initial phone call and scheduling the appointment to the completion of the patient encounter. The consultants will take a critical look at access, staffing, productivity and customer service to determine:

- How patient services can be improved;
- What duplication or redundant processes exist;

- If resources are being optimized; and
- How productivity can be increased.

Access

Access often emerges as one of the major issues that must be addressed in the faculty practice. Patients frequently complain about the length of time they wait to be seen. The wait for a new patient visit in some specialties exceeds 30 days, and a return patient is likely to wait 20 days or more. Instead of waiting for an appointment, patients sometimes go elsewhere, creating a missed opportunity for the practice. Exploring the reason for poor access and the effect it has on patient satisfaction and financial performance is paramount to understanding what actions should be taken.

Productivity and Managing the Scheduling System

Addressing access issues and physician productivity begins with managing the entire scheduling system, not just the scheduling of patients. The outpatient scheduling system should maximize the facility by deploying the appropriate number of physicians for every clinic session. Simply put, if each physician needs to toggle between 3 exam rooms and there are 15 exam rooms in the clinic, five physicians should be scheduled to work in the clinic every session. In my experience, this is not a reality, nor is it given importance.

Academic physicians are scheduled to work in the outpatient clinics when it does not compromise their competing priorities of teaching, research and administration. The availability to conduct clinic sessions is constantly changing as research grants are sought, research projects ensue, conferences are scheduled and the physicians' teaching responsibilities shift throughout the year. While it certainly doesn't happen in every faculty practice, it is nonetheless not uncommon for physicians to cancel clinic sessions for weeks, even months at a time. If other physicians are not assigned to fill the vacant slots, clinic space, physician productivity and patient access suffer.

In reality, an already pent-up demand for patient access increases, revenue declines and customer service plummets when physicians cancel their sessions. For the most part, management either skirts this issue or has been unsuccessful in developing collaborative efforts with physicians to overcome this looming problem. Expectations and standards are not applied for maintaining scheduled sessions. No limit has been established for the number of sessions that may be canceled. This leaves the clinic with an unmanaged scheduling system that does not match supply with demand. In the overall scheme, this represents a substantial loss in revenue, when expenses remain consistent.

In some instances, the scheduling system is further compromised because there simply aren't enough physicians to meet the demand. If the physical capacity can accommodate additional providers, the use of mid-level extenders proves to be an excellent way to fill vacant sessions and improve access, as long as the physicians and management support this concept.

Other complications that contribute to an unmanaged scheduling system are physicians that move their sessions to a more convenient day, without particular concern for the availability of space or the imposition to patients or support staff. They may arrive at the clinic with a full schedule only to discover they are competing for exam rooms. These physicians are now waiting for exam rooms with their patients backing up. This happens because too many doctors are vying for too few exam rooms. Yet, there are other days when the clinic space is under-utilized because physicians have cancelled their sessions. A well managed scheduling system that optimizes space results in reduced frustration for physicians and patients, and improves the clinic's financial position.

Optimizing Clinical Sessions

The economics of optimizing clinical space can be explored by developing the maximum revenue projections, built from internal assumptions that consider pre-determined average revenue per patient and multiply this number by the maximum number of patients that can be accommodated in the facility.

Example: Let's assume the outpatient clinic can accommodate five physicians in sessions simultaneously, and each half-day session consists of three hours. If the physician-scheduling template accommodates three patients per hour, the maximum number of patients that could be seen in one physician's session would be nine. We'll use a modest figure of $125.00 for the average revenue per patient visit.

> 5 MDs $\times$ 2 sessions/day = 10 sessions/day
> 3 patient visits/hour $\times$ 3 hours/session = 9
> Average revenue/patient visit = $125
> 10 $\times$ 9 x $125 = $11,250 daily revenue

When this number is multiplied by five days a week and 50 weeks a year (eliminating an estimated two weeks a year when the clinic is closed for holidays), the total annual revenue in this example would be $2,812,500, for an allocation of five full-time-equivalent physicians to serve the clinic.

Another factor that influences the ability to optimize the clinic and obtain an improved financial outcome is missed appointments—the no shows and late cancellations that are not filled. In my experience, it is not uncommon for faculty practices to have a missed appointment rate between 24% and 38%. This occurs at the same time patients calling for appointments are required to wait an unrealistic amount of time to see a physician, because "the schedule is full." Faculty practices must consider these missed appointments as substantial lost revenue and a deterrent to patient satisfaction.

Missed appointments also result in increased overhead related to staff time involved with the intended patient visit. The employee activities required for each scheduled appointment include taking the initial phone call, scheduling the appointment, locating and preparing the chart, reviewing demographics, preparing a charge ticket, documenting the no show, calling the patient to reschedule and returning the chart to the file system. These steps have all been taken for a visit that does not take place and does not generate revenue for the practice. Add to this the lost physician productivity and allocating clinical resources and space based on scheduled patients, and the economics of the missed appointment are dismal.

Missed appointments also restrict other patients' ability to obtain an appointment in a clinic where the demand often exceeds access. In other words, patients are vying to get into the clinic at the same time there are holes in the schedule, because of no shows and late cancellations. Improving access so that patients can be seen in the clinic sooner contributes to a reduction in missed appointments. Results are further improved when an effective appointment-confirmation system is in place.

Building a well-managed scheduling system dramatically improves physician productivity, patient access and profitability. In order to accomplish this, systems and processes must be in place to accommodate the increased productivity. This is where centralization becomes the clinic's ally. If some of the responsibilities for running the clinic are shifted to centralized services, information and needs will be better managed, and the remaining activities of running the outpatient facility can be given the attention that is needed to serve the patients better.

Staffing

Shifting responsibilities related to the clinic from the physician's secretary to clinic staff will succeed with proper planning and clear delineation of duties. Removing these duties from the secretaries allows them to focus on academic endeavors. When clinical staff members assume the clinic-related duties, it promotes increased efficiency, improved outcomes and better control. It is important that staff resources be properly allocated to ensure the workload is evenly distributed.

When positions are designed by area of specialty (i.e., scheduling, phone coverage, medical records, patient registration), individuals are more likely to become "experts" at their job—rather than jacks-of-all-trades, but mastering none. Specialization increases staff confidence and improves performance. This does not mean employees should not be cross-trained. By all means, this is important to smooth patient flow and supporting their co-workers. When the workload is well distributed and the staff is confident and capable, functional work teams develop. Members of the work teams respect each other's contribution and learn to depend on each other, which results in better patient services.

Developing well-defined job descriptions helps clarify the duties each person will perform and lists the primary responsibilities for the position. The job description should also describe the qualifications of the position—education, skills and experience. The job description must also describe the physical demands of the position, as required by the Americans with Disabilities Act. In addition to listing the major tasks under the job responsibilities, it is advisable to include a final line item "and other duties as assigned." This discourages the "it's not in my job description" attitude.

The organization's objectives and mission can be reinforced by establishing performance standards that support these. Let's say one of the objectives is to be more patient-focused. If the staff is expected to be courteous and helpful to patients in support of this objective, you may want a standard for the receptionist that states patients will be greeted with a smile and by name within 30 seconds of their arrival. Further state that this expectation must be met 95% of the time. Of course, the performance must then be monitored to be sure the employee meets the expectation.

E-fficiency

Most faculty practices lead the way in implementing technology to improve operational efficiency. Physicians and staff are hooked up to the Internet and intranets. Unfortunately, many people are not making the leap to use the computer to expedite and improve communication. Interoffice e-mail and instant messaging need to replace getting up from a workstation to talk to someone or using the telephone.

Many clinics have moved toward electronic health records (EHRs), commonly referred to as "electronic medical records." Some of these practices still hold on to the hard copy of the patient's chart. If the EHR software has the capability to eliminate the hard copy record, steps should be taken to accomplish this.

Hand-held computers are instrumental in helping physicians' access information, report their charges and reduce the time involved with these tasks. This contributes to timely and accurate charge entry, reduces the potential for dropping charges, eliminates concern about misplaced charge tickets and saves staff time. The software is generally user-friendly, reducing problems inherent with the learning curve.

E-prescribing has been particularly helpful in managing patient prescriptions and saving time. When this is tied to the EHR, functions are enhanced, and the time savings can be substantial.

Patients can add to the clinic's efficiency when they are Internet savvy and the faculty practice has expanded its technology to include patient participation. Patients can go to the website to learn more about the faculty practice and the scope of services that are offered. They can obtain maps that reduce the need to obtain oral directions to the facility. Many medical organizations have implemented technology that allows patients to pre-register and schedule appointments online. These various features promote efficiency, improve communication and service and contribute to cost containment. Once a website is patient-friendly and able to improve patient services, the staff must be trained to direct patients to the website.

CUSTOMER SERVICE

Customer service in the medical facility is measured by patient satisfaction, and how satisfied the patient is in the academic setting is questionable. It begins with poor access, as previously discussed, but moves beyond that to an attitude that can permeate the clinic. Physicians may have an attitude of superiority that patients can sense. Support staff, on the other hand, may take a come-what-may attitude; "I'm just doing my job; this is the way it is, and there's nothing I can do about it."

These attitudes are damaging to the reputation of the academic practice and result in patient dissatisfaction. Patients already have to deal with frustration in waiting for an appointment, driving out of their own community, difficulty with parking and meandering through a large campus to find the outpatient clinic where they are scheduled. Add to this that the person greeting them is perfunctory with no interest in or sensitivity to the patients' situation, and patients are bound to be discontented.

Conducting Surveys

Customer service reports in faculty practices may be skewed by the methodology employed to measure patient satisfaction. Often the surveys are completed and collected at the clinic. This survey technique can result in the same individual repeatedly responding to the survey. It also limits the sampling to voluntary participation. This creates an inability to know if the sampling is representative of the clinic population served. The survey results become biased, unreliable and useless.

It is suggested that patient satisfaction surveys be conducted and analyzed by a professional surveyor, unrelated to the organization. Although this requires an investment, it is essential to obtaining and analyzing quantitative information that is reliable. Once baseline results are acquired, the practice can establish defined improvement goals.

Dispute Resolution

Developing standardized dispute-resolution processes offers an opportunity to obtain qualitative information about patients' complaints. An incident report needs to be completed with each dispute. The report should describe the complaint and the measures taken to resolve it. When a control copy is kept on file, the clinic can review the issues that emerged, the action taken, which staff member handled the situation and the time frame required to take corrective action. To improve efficiency and save time, the documentation processes can be automated. By reviewing trends over time, an internal report card emerges. This gives the clinic the opportunity to examine its own commitment to customer satisfaction.

The Commitment

A commitment to patient satisfaction and customer service does not happen overnight, and it is not the result of a workshop or a trendy customer service byline. A commitment to patient satisfaction must be demonstrated at the top. Seeing patients on time, being approachable and listening to their needs goes a long way in achieving patient satisfaction. Support staff will take their lead from the physicians, but must be held to a standard that treats patients with dignity and respect. When patient satisfaction is woven into the performance review, support staff will take notice.

Patients are attracted to the academic medical center because of its reputation as a leading innovative medical research and teaching institution. It's important that the patient believes the physicians are approachable and the clinic is a "caring" place.

BUILDING TRUST

Cultural, economic and operational changes cannot be accomplished without a foundation of trust. The ingredients for trust are grounded in our behavior, personal integrity and respect. Obtaining a commitment and cooperation is dependent on listening and responding to the other person's needs and objections. Trust is gained when those commitments are honored and both parties are working toward a mutual goal.

FACING CHANGE

It's a bold step forward to face change head-on, knowing it takes us to places unknown. Just the same, unless we are willing to examine what has changed in and around us, and look at the implications, we will not be able to progress and make the most of the future. This is true whether you are a revered academic physician, a computer analyst, administrator, supervisor, medical assistant or file clerk.

Many academic faculty practices have the advantage of skilled administrators focused on helping them succeed in a changing environment. Once the relationship is grounded with trust, physicians and administration have an opportunity to create a new, dynamic performance model— one that relates to physicians'needs, business essentials and customer service. Times are changing, and we all must adjust in order to progress and be a part of the future.

There are a few things that are paramount to the ability to accept and endorse change. Each person must:
1. Believe the change is for the better and the outcome is worth the effort;
2. Be flexible enough to adapt to change; and

3. Contribute to achieving the desired result.

If we do not contribute to the change process, we may, directly or indirectly, sabotage the results. Sabotage is not unfamiliar to the change agent, and it is often a result of suspicious attitudes, inflexibility or arrogance. It is overcome when everyone involved in an effort pulls together to accomplish a goal. This is certainly more difficult to achieve in large academic practices, where some employees may lack a strong commitment to the organization. Management must make every effort to build relationships with line staff members that will contribute to staff's sense of belonging and increase their commitment.

MAKING A DIFFERENCE

When Marcy Hall, the Administrator for the department of radiology at an east coast university medical center, discovered that the lack of knowledge and communication in her department was leading to disruptive clinics, as well as disruptive behavior, she explored opportunities to resolve these problems and monitor progress to be sure there would not be a repeat performance.

Marcy realized problems were brewing in her department when she observed morale deteriorating among the administrative staff, the residents and the faculty. Clearly there were troublesome communication issues among them that resulted in a lack of understanding and mutual support, causing friction within the clinic.

Communication in the Multi-Mission Department

It was early in 2008, and the residents and faculty were feeling uninformed about what was going on in the clinic. At the same time, the clinic's operational staff members felt they were facing unrealistic demands from the clinic physicians.

At that time, the standard communication channels within the department consisted of the following processes:

- There were separate formal orientation programs for residents, faculty and clinical support staff.
- The Clinic Office Manager had meetings with clerical staff on a monthly basis. These meetings focused on operational issues as they related to patient schedules, front desk operations and billing procedures and policies. Information from the medical center was disseminated when it affected their tasks.

- The Clinic Nurse Manager met monthly with the clinical support staff. These meetings focused on the clinical operations of the department that related to the clinical staff. The purpose of these meetings was to share information that was pertinent to patient care and information from the medical center as it pertained to patient care.
- The Department Administrator met with the two clinic managers on a monthly basis. These meetings allowed the administrative team to review processes, share concerns, brainstorm solutions, share information and make sure that clinical operations were running efficiently. Information from other university departments was also shared during this time to keep the managers aware of what was happening.
- The Resident Program Director met with residents and the Residency Program Coordinator. However, the focus of these meetings was clinical in nature and did not focus on administrative matters. Rather, they concentrated on resident concerns related to the entire residency program.

The separate orientation programs were not coordinated among the various groups nor was information communicated, which in essence got new people off to a less than satisfactory start in developing relationships and having realistic expectations of each other. Administrative staff ended up "picking up the pieces." This became evident as working relationships deteriorated in the spring of 2008.

In one of the Administrative Managers' meetings, the managers reported that support staff was complaining about the staff physicians working in the clinic. They were concerned that faculty did not acknowledge them by name, and that residents were unhappy with the content of their messages and tasks that were communicated by the front desk. The physicians also weren't happy with the way patients were scheduled during their individual clinic sessions and were being disruptive when things didn't suit them. It was time to resolve these disruptive situations and improve relationships.

These issues were brought up in a discussion with the Chair and Senior Administrator, and a decision was made to establish a working team consisting of the Clinical Medical Director, Senior Administrator, Nurse Manager, Office Manager and Chief Resident.

This was the beginning of collaboration among those that could implement change. The goal was to work toward improving communication and solving the growing dissention among all members of the clinical team.

Initially those involved were territorial. "There were push backs and attempts to build walls instead of bridges," Marcy said, but progress was made, and concrete, doable solutions emerged.

The outcome from this interactive discussion led to the development of a defined set of problems that needed to be addressed. As part of the solution process, a template was created to address the various communication problems. This resulted in a final template that described the major problems and the actions the attendees collectively agreed to take to resolve each of these problems. It addressed:

1. Residents' communication with support staff;
2. Faculty communication with support staff;
3. Boundaries of communication; and
4. Patient flow.

This was then expanded into the Problem-Solving Worksheet that included a comments column. The team had two different meetings to review the plan and make adjustments until a final plan was accepted and implemented.

Execution

Initially, the team met every two weeks, using the Problem-Solving Worksheet as a tool to monitor progress on resolution of issues. At first, simple solutions were identified for the problems that were easiest to solve. These were immediately communicated to all clinical members to implement. The remaining problems took longer to resolve but were worked through diligently. Communication and respect among all participants emerged. Finally, clinics began to run more smoothly. Efforts were made to commence clinical sessions on time, and messages sent to the physicians were more accurate. Eventually, tasks were completed more efficiently, and the clinical area settled down.

The team continues to meet on a monthly basis and review what has been occurring in clinic sessions. When problems emerge, group members will brainstorm, determine solutions and go back to their respective employees to implement the changes. This has become an ongoing process.

The outcomes of these meetings flow to other members of the department through their individual monthly meetings. A new culture has emerged with greatly improved communication and teamwork.

What Others Can Learn

• Recognize the new culture of residency rotation—the 8 to 5 mentality.

- Place the right players in position of authority. They can take the problem matrix to their own staff, listen to staff members' input and revise the recommended solution as they see fit.
- Collaborative thinking turns to action when the players are invested.
- Managers need to be willing and able to follow the matrices, oversee progress and maintain accountability.
- It will remain a work in progress as relationships continue to be nurtured, strengthening a spirit of cooperation and trust through open communication.

This case study reinforces the reality that when leadership and the stakeholders involved in an issue come together and are committed to resolving a problem, there is an opportunity to achieve success in changing a culture and deepening respect among layers of an organization. This requires patience and a common vision for progress.

THE SECRETS

1. Acknowledge the competing priorities of academic physicians.
2. Revised compensation plans are designed to increase academic physicians' commitment to serve in the outpatient clinic.
3. Centralized services are intended to improve the clinic's operational and financial performance.
4. Academic faculty practices can expect to be self-sustaining without compromising physicians' academic pursuits.
5. An unbiased operational assessment provides a blueprint to help the academic faculty practice meet its stated goals.
6. Optimizing clinical space is critical to improving clinic productivity and enhancing revenue.
7. A commitment to patient satisfaction begins at the top.
8. Trust is critical to building collaborative working relationships.
9. Accountability needs to be built into the system to get results.
10. Changing a culture requires a commitment of each stakeholder.

FORMS ADDED TO YOUR TOOLBOX:

- *Problem-Solving Worksheet*
- *Risk/Opportunity Matrix*
- *Sample Performance Standards Worksheet*

CHAPTER 9

The Power of Revenue Management

R evenue management is a multifaceted process; and, as with every area of practice performance, the greater the commitment, the greater the result. It takes an organized approach that starts before patients select their physician and ends with the final payment.

Getting paid for what they do remains one of the biggest concerns for physicians and administrators across the country. This concern exists for academic practices, group practices (both small and large) and solo physicians. There's no one big secret, but there are many little secrets and actions that are worthy of administrator and physician attention to improve revenue performance.

> **KEY FACT:** *Getting paid more for what you do depends on a multitude of decisions and begins before the patient is seen.*

CAPTURING CHARGES

When I ask physicians to describe the process of capturing charges, they tell me it's a matter of documenting all the services on the office or hospital charge ticket or the EHR and being sure the charges are entered into the billing system. These are vital processes to capturing charges, but there are other factors that play an important role in increasing revenue by capturing more charges. It begins with contracting.

Contracting Issues

There are physicians that do their own contracting and those that delegate some or all of this responsibility to managed care organizations (MCOs) through a centralized management service organization or independent physician association (IPA). Physicians that have relinquished the control of contracting to a third party have done so because of convenience, fear of not being able to get an individual contract or concern about the ability to obtain the best contract terms on their own. These third parties may or may not be effective at representing physicians and obtaining favorable fee schedules or payment terms. Furthermore, they sometimes fail to provide the practice with copies of the contracts and associated fee schedules.

It's the responsibility of the practice to evaluate and monitor the performance of the third-party payers and hold them to the terms of the contract. If you are considering contracting through an IPA or MCO, it is essential to hold it accountable to provide the practice with documentation and fees schedules for each contract. I am amazed by how many times I've encountered a practice that either does not have copies of contracts and related fee schedules or has them but does not know where they are. How can such a practice be sure it is getting paid correctly and that the terms of the contract are not being violated? Physicians and staff cannot enforce the contract and have no means to hold the payer accountable unless they have a copy of the contract and its supporting documents.

Take a critical look at the insurance companies you contract with or intend to contract with in the future. Just because a new payer arrives on the scene doesn't mean you need to jump on board and obtain a contract. Look at the potential impact before you sign on. Does this insurance company or MCO have a contract with an important employer in town? Will further physician referrals be jeopardized if you don't sign on? What are the implications to the practice and your existing patients if you do or don't sign on?

Physicians have too often allowed insurance plans to dictate fees and terms of contracts in the past, but that doesn't mean they need to do so in the future. It's time to take back control. Scrutinize every contract you are considering. Don't let the emotions of the situation get the best of you, even if the insurance company appears to be a major player in town. The goal in working with insurance payers is to develop a good relationship and contracts that are acceptable with terms that do not compromise either the practice or its patients.

Fees are negotiable. Ask to see the plan's fees for the top 10 to 20 codes utilized by the practice—and don't sign the contract otherwise. Financial vulnerability and potential risk exist in not knowing how much you will be paid and when. If you don't ask for more, you're not going to get it, and it must be done before signing the contract.

Don't assume that you are locked into the terms of some boilerplate contract that's being passed around to all the doctors in town. Learn to say no to terms that aren't acceptable. For example, a contract may require a physician to submit claims within 60 days of service, but may not specify a time limit on when the payer actually pays the physician. Why would a physician agree to those terms? Of course, there is some protection if your state has legislation that requires the insurance plan to pay clean claims within a certain number of days. Check your state's Prompt Payment Laws before you agree to a contract that does not specify payment terms.

Keep in mind that the relevant documents mentioned in the contract, not just the contract itself, should be examined. Physicians need a clear understanding of the grievance process from the start, not once a problem emerges. Review the plan's quality assurance and utilization management procedures. Find out what the plan expects from the practice and what the practice will be agreeing to once the contract is finalized. What are the call-coverage requirements? Also get a clear understanding of the medical liability the practice will own under the contract. Does it include a hold-harmless clause to protect the physicians and the practice? It's wise to have the contract reviewed by your malpractice carrier and/or lawyer in advance.

Turn to professional organizations for guidance in reviewing contracts. The Professional Association of Health Care Office Management, Medical Group Management Association (MGMA), state medical associations and specialty societies have tools to help medical practices examine and understand an insurance contract and its implications.

Keep Staff Informed

Once the contract has been signed, someone in the office must assume responsibility for educating the staff about the essentials. Make sure you have the answers to these questions *before* patients arrive in the office:

1. Are all the physicians/providers contracted with the plan?
2. What are the data collection requirements?
3. Is pre-authorization required, and if so, are services limited to consultation or are diagnostic studies and follow-up included in the authorization?
4. Can benefits verification, eligibility, pre-authorization and the referral process be handled online?
5. What are the patient's responsibilities, and, if the patient fails to meet these responsibilities, what action is the practice permitted to take?

6. What services are NOT covered by the contract?
7. For noncovered services, can payment be collected from the patient when the services are rendered, or is the practice required to submit a claim that is denied by the payer before it can collect from the patient?
8. What are the billing requirements, including time limits, where claims are submitted and if substantiating documents are required?
9. Who is the plan's provider-relations contact for the office, and what is that person's direct phone number?
10. What happens if the plan becomes insolvent?
11. What is the fee schedule?

Too often, staff members don't have a copy of the fee schedule for the plan. If your billing department assumes the practice is being paid correctly and posts the payment and adjustment accordingly, it may be absorbing losses for underpayments. This can cost the practice many thousands of dollars each month. I've seen it happen all too often. Remember: A well-informed staff guards the practice's financial interest.

PATIENT REGISTRATION

There's power in the patient registration process. Respect it! The patient registration form is the patients' first financial document in the practice and is vital for making sure the practice gets paid. The form must be user-friendly. Use words the patients recognize. If patients are complaining about completing or updating the form and ask questions that demonstrate confusion, redesign the form. Make sure the form is system-friendly, too. Because staff members are accustomed to viewing the registration information on screen, they can quickly spot missing data if the patient registration form simulates the computer registration screen. This will result in a faster and more accurate registration process.

Educate, enforce and reinforce the importance of patient registration. This means holding staff and patients accountable. The staff must take responsibility for obtaining accurate patient registration information *at each visit*. Patients must do their part by providing you with the information. There are important questions to ask established patients at each visit. Keeping patient registration information current depends on how these questions are asked. There's a right way and a wrong way (Table 1).

This matrix should be part of the staff training and remain the mantra for keeping insurance information current at each visit. If there are changes,

TABLE 1. Right and Wrong Ways to Ask for Patient Information

Information Needed	Right Way to Ask	Wrong Way to Ask
Current phone number	Please confirm your home and work phone numbers for me.	Are your phone numbers the same?
Current address	Are you still living at 312 Windy Drive?	Is your address the same?
Employer	Are you still employed by the City of New York?	Have you changed jobs?
Insurance	Is Aetna Preferred still your primary insurance? Do you still have secondary insurance coverage with United Healthcare?	Do you still have the same primary and secondary insurance?
Insurance	Is this visit due to a workers' compensation or auto injury?	Not asking about the possibility of injury.

input them in the computer system when the questions are asked—and get an updated copy of the patient's insurance card. If you don't have one, purchase a card scanner to scan patients' insurance cards. This keeps the document in an electronic file that is accurate and can easily be retrieved—and its eco-friendly.

Working in real-time ensures accuracy. The billing office, nurses and doctors can pull up the patient's account or electronic health record (EHR) and have the most accurate demographic information, which helps them when ordering tests or making treatment decisions.

CHARGE REPORTING

Most practices that have implemented EHRs have wisely done away with the charge ticket—a primary step to shredding the paper monster and obtaining provider commitment to document in real-time during the patient visit.

For those practices without EHRs, the encounter form (charge ticket) should be reviewed annually and scrutinized for potential change. Are all the codes updated to comply with the latest versions of both CPT® and

ICD-9? Does it make sense, is it multifunctional? Does it contribute to ease in documenting the visit, data entry, scheduling follow-up care and collecting payment? Too often, charge tickets have detailed printed information that serves little purpose in documenting the encounter. Here are a few suggestions in designing a functional form:

- Make sure patient demographics and insurance information appear at the top of the form.
- List only the top office CPT® codes, based on actual utilization. (Utilization data can be pulled from the computer system for the past 12 months to guide this process.)
- Do not place hospital services on the office charge ticket.
- Leave a space for staff instructions (i.e., what diagnostic studies need to be scheduled and when the patient needs to return to the office).
- Designate an area to document the payment received and the balance on the account.

When it comes to reporting hospital charges, many physicians fall short by not completing the charge document in real-time. This can be a major contributor to inaccurate coding, lost charges, duplication of effort, staff inefficiency and delayed billing. I once worked with a gastroenterology practice that failed to charge for 15% of its hospital procedures, a total of more than $100,000 a year, because the physicians failed to report these procedures to the billing department. The potential for this to occur is greatly reduced with implementation of an EHR system that allows physicians to access patient charts off-site and record services rendered from a regular computer or PDA.

Accurate and timely charge submission is the responsibility of the person performing the service. Providers should not be delegating this function to someone else in the office, whether it is done with paper and pen or an EHR.

Coding Accuracy

Every practice needs a resident coding expert on staff, preferably a Certified Professional Coder. The coding expert examines charge activity to be sure visits are coded properly (both ICD-9 and CPT®, including modifiers). Empower your coder to assume responsibility for educating physicians and staff. When finding inaccurate or incomplete charge documentation, the coder can use these examples to conduct a coding review for physicians and staff so the coding errors are not repeated.

REVENUE RECOVERY

Once the practice has taken the appropriate steps in capturing and reporting charges, the revenue-recovery process begins, and the actions taken can either improve or impede cash flow. If claims are accurate with timely submission, it will result in improved cash flow, which is sped up even more with electronic claims payment. Incomplete claims or inaccurate payments result in duplication of effort, inefficiency and slower payment. This increases practice expenses at the same time revenue is being delayed. Quality claims submission remains paramount to improved revenue-recovery processes.

Set revenue-recovery standards in the office. Establish what you consider to be reasonable and acceptable. Provide the tools and support necessary to meet these guidelines, and then hold staff accountable based on the standards. Here are some examples:

- **Accurate claims submission:** This can be measured by the number of claims that are rejected by your clearinghouse or insurance plans. Determine an acceptable error ratio, but keep the standard high (i.e., less than 3% to 5%). Errors can be traced and used for staff education and accountability. For example, if the patient's date of birth or insurance plan numbers cannot be identified, an error has been made in collecting the data or entering it into the system. Also establish a turnaround standard such as a rejected claim must be properly resubmitted as a clean claim within 72 hours, and exceptions must be justified. With electronic charge reporting, these time frames can be reduced.
- **Timely claims submission:**
  - Charge entry   Office: 1 to 2 days

                          Inpatient: 2 to 5 days

                          Surgery: 2 to 5 days
  - Billing submission   Office: 3 to 4 days

                          Inpatient: 4 to 7 days

                          Surgery: 4 to 7 days

Of course, charge entry and claims submission may take longer if you are assisting a physician that is not in your practice since you don't have control of his or her charge entry process and your coding and fee must comply with the primary physician's.

- **Timely claims payment:** If claims are submitted accurately, payment should reach the office within 30 to 45 days.
- **Accurate and timely patient billing:**
  - Once a claim is paid by the insurance company and the required contract adjustment is made, the balance should be transferred to patient responsibility immediately.
  - Patient statements should be generated within 30 days of transferring to patient responsibility. The timeliest method to accomplish prompt billing is cycle billing: separating the patient accounts into four alphabetical batches and billing each batch during a different week of the month. This also spreads out patient calls to the billing department regarding statements.
  - Co-pays must be paid at the time of service.
  - Patient balances should be collected:
    — If and when the patient returns to the office; or
    — Within 30 days of the patient receiving a statement.
    — For larger balances, develop payment plan standards that get you paid within six months.

Practices that fail to establish written revenue-recovery standards are jeopardizing the ability to improve cash flow and optimize revenue.

MONITORING PERFORMANCE

The power of revenue management includes monitoring internal and external performance—what physicians, staff, patients, MCOs and insurance plans are doing that impact revenue and whether intervention is required.

Conducting Chart Audits

One of the most effective ways to analyze performance with charge reporting and payer payments is the chart audit. Conducting audits is also a key component to an effective compliance program. Practices can implement their own procedures to accomplish this, but they will be most effective when these procedures involve physicians and staff. If teams are formed with a receptionist or scheduler, nurse, physician and someone from the billing department, the cross representation and broader knowledge result in a better audit. It also serves as an educational process and provides greater understanding of everyone's contribution to revenue management. The resident coder or your compliance officer should serve as the project manager.

Pull five to 10 random charts for each physician and mid-level provider to obtain a broad range of patient types, services and payers. For each patient, select one day's encounter, going back at least eight weeks prior to the date of the audit. For each selected encounter, additional information must be collected:

- Appointment record;
- Chart documentation (chart notes) for the visit;
- Encounter form;
- Patient ledger (itemization of charges, adjustments and payments); and
- Explanation of benefits (EOB).

Carefully review and compare each document looking for any discrepancies. The appointment record and chart note should match dates and patient name. If the chart belongs to John T. Smith and the documentation states the encounter took place on April 3, be sure John T. Smith appears on the appointment schedule, not John A. Smith, an entirely different patient. Such a discrepancy would require further research to correct.

The documentation on the chart notes must validate the services appearing on the charge ticket including date of service, diagnosis and procedure codes for the visit and other ancillary services. Review the chart and verify that reports are in the file and that they have been read and signed off on by the physician.

The charges on the charge ticket should mirror charges appearing on the patient ledger. This audit process confirms that no data entry errors were made and no charges were missed or altered.

The final step is a review of the EOB to verify that the insurance plan processed the claim and reimbursed for the services properly. Insurance companies make errors—make it your responsibility to find them. Errors in adjudicating claims should be caught by the billing department when posting the payment, but your audit will serve as a double check and reinforce accountability.

If errors are detected during the audit, estimate the cost to the practice. If the audit reveals a potential gain of 12% on evaluation and management (E&M) services, calculate this against the revenue for those procedures over the past year. For example, if E&M office codes represented $265,000 of last year's revenue, an additional 12% would be nearly $32,000. That's not small change!

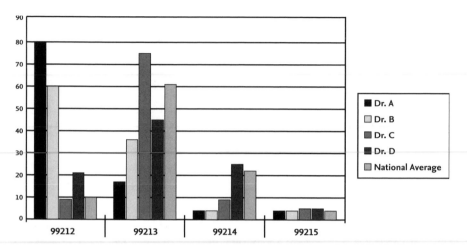

FIGURE 1. Physician charge patterns analysis. E&M coding: internal medicine.

The first chart audit becomes the baseline for improving performance and educating both providers and staff. Periodic audits should be built into your system to measure progress and ensure compliance.

If an internal audit results in substantial errors throughout the various departments, it may be best to bring in a coding and reimbursement specialist to train staff and implement effective revenue management policies and procedures. Don't be shortsighted by focusing on the costs to accomplish this—the investment can pay big dividends.

Coding Patterns

Examine and compare the E&M coding patterns of the physicians by pulling the top 10 encounter codes for both hospital and office visits. Compare this with the national utilization of E&M codes, available through the MGMA or Medicare, which publishes E&M coding statistics by specialty. The MGMA provides broader and more meaningful numbers, because its reports include various patient age groups, not just Medicare patients. These reports also break down key CPT® codes by diagnosis, which enables the practice to dig deeper into coding practices (Figure 1).

This peer-review process proves helpful in identifying physicians that may be too aggressive or too cautious in the way they apply E&M codes and whether the group may be incurring risk exposure as a result of a physician's coding practices. At the same time, if one physician seems to be on the mark with proper coding, he or she can help other physicians extend their knowledge of coding application.

Identifying the Poor-Performing Payer

The practice administrator takes the lead role in looking out for the practice's interests when dealing with insurance plans or MCOs. It is prudent to implement procedures to monitor payer performance and decide which insurance plans should be continued or truncated. Maybe it's time to identify the bottom-feeders and cancel those managed care contracts that are more trouble than they are worth. This strategy has merit, but requires analysis to identify which payers are the culprits that wreak havoc on the practice, and whether it makes sense to eliminate them. Use the following as a guide:

1. **Examine the hassle factor.** The manager and insurance biller will need to examine key indicators and past performance patterns of third-party payers. A look at these four key indicators will identify the payers that give the most hassle:

   - *The plan requires repeated requests for referral or authorization.* Look for the payers (insurance plans or MCOs) that physicians and staff struggle with or that require excessive time to deal with.

   - *Claims are processed slowly.* If there are payers that repeatedly reject clean claims or ask for information that has already been provided or is not necessary to process the claim, put these payers on the hassle list.

   - *Patients complain about their insurance company.* When patients come to a physician or staff member complaining about poor service from their insurance company, listen. This can be a sign of trouble. The payer may be cutting staff because it cannot meet its bottom line. On the other hand, it may not have invested in the infrastructure required to support its members and maintain viability.

   - *Provider-relations support is substandard.* If staff members are frustrated with the lack of support they receive from provider relations or the inability to get their questions answered, the payer may be more trouble than it is worth.

   Rate each payer, giving it one point for each "yes" it receives on the above hassle factors. A zero rating represents an excellent payer in terms of the hassle factor.

2. **Review the outstanding claims reports.** For several months in a row, generate and review the outstanding claims report. This will identify the payers that account for the highest volume of outstanding claims and those that account for the largest amount of revenue due on outstanding claims. The top five may be the same or may be varied. If, for example, one payer appears each month that accounts for a high volume of claims, but not a major amount of revenue, you may want to act on it. Canceling this contract may not have significant financial repercussions, but might save valuable staff time. However, before determining this, check out the referring source for these patients. If it turns out to be an important referring physician, discuss the situation with him or her before you act. Communicating up-front can reduce the chances of alienating referring physicians.

3. **Assess reimbursement rates.** Based on the top 10 CPT® codes utilization for the practice, develop a spreadsheet on payer performance. A sample is provided in the tool box (see Payer Performance Table in the Toolbox). This will identify the variable payments of different plans and reveal the poorer-paying contracts. When the troublesome payers have been identified, assess the potential impact of eliminating any or all of these payers. Measure this impact with the following points in mind:

   - Volume of business the payer represents;
   - Impact on existing and potential patients;
   - Loss of revenue and long-term economic effect;
   - Existing scheduling needs (perhaps eliminating a few payers will open up time on the schedule to see more patients from other better-paying sources); and
   - Political issues that may exist with referring physicians (perhaps they are considering dropping a poor payer or feel compelled to provide service to a poor payer for reasons that are unknown to you).

If you decide to fire some of the payers based on your findings, drop the worst payer first and measure the impact. Begin by reviewing the existing contract to be sure the terms required for termination are not violated. Decide how to communicate your intention to drop the plan to referring physicians and patients who are members of the plan. It will be important to continue providing care for plan patients under treatment. Of course, you can offer to see patients out of network. This means you will submit claims on their behalf, but you are not willing to accept the fee schedule the plan has presented to you.

Be sure no one in the practice makes negative comments about the payer to patients or other practices. It serves no purpose and takes away from the professionalism of the practice.

Even if your analysis results in a decision not to fire any existing payers, examining these key indicators provides a basis to monitor payer performance over time. It also puts the practice in a knowledgeable position that holds payers accountable to meet specific expectations.

Office Collections

Collecting from patients when they are in the office is referred to as over-the-counter (OTC) payment. Effective OTC collection requires staff members to assume responsibility for collecting patient payments whenever patients have an appointment.

More employers are cutting health insurance benefits by switching to insurance plans with larger deductibles and those that require patients to assume a bigger share of the costs. This makes it incredibly important for medical practices throughout the country to take a firmer stance on patient collections.

If the practice doesn't implement tight collection procedures, it is likely to end up with a rising accounts receivable (A/R). Receptionists at both the receiving and exit stations should be trained in how to review a patient's billing and payment record on the computer and understand what the patient owes. Then it will be easier to hold them accountable for optimizing collecting from patients—both co-pays and existing patient balances.

Increased accountability is best accomplished when the batch of daily charge tickets is reviewed, comparing OTC payments with the amount patients actually owed. Establish OTC collection goals, and review them with the receptionists. If they have difficulty asking for money, they can observe another staffer that excels in this area. They can also do some role playing. I once worked with a four-physician urology practice that doubled OTC payments within 30 days once staff members were trained. The physicians were impressed as the receptionists continued to increase the amount they collected. The doctors complimented the receptionists on their progress. This was enough motivation to keep the staff confident and focused on raising the bar. Just think of how much time and money were saved by not having to send out repeated statements and reducing the

TABLE 2. Recovering Aged Receivables

Balance on account: $1,000 = 100%	
Age of Charge	Amount Likely to be Collected
30 days	$950 = 95%
90 days	$750 = 75%
180 days	$300 = 30%

amount of time staff spent following up on patient balances, as they continue to age and become less collectible.

Patients are far more motivated to take responsibility for paying their doctors when they still remember how much they needed them. If you wait too long before getting serious about asking for payment, the treatment the patients received may be a faded memory.

It has been suggested by some experts that that the chance of getting paid is reduced substantially the longer the charge is on the books. Table 2 offers an example of what this might mean to the practice:

Give staff members clear direction on expectations, and let them help you in determining specific measurement of their progress. This will help them take ownership and support their success.

The most effective way to achieve the target OTC collection goal is to establish graduated expectations for improvement over a specific period of time (Table 3).

Each week, monitor staff members' performance with OTC payments, and share the results with them. Continue to encourage and praise them as they progress. Some practices offer bonuses when targets are hit, as an incentive to improve collections.

If staff members struggle to hit the targets, provide additional support to teach them the skills necessary to obtain patient payments and over-

TABLE 3. OTC Collection Goals

OTC Payments	Average Daily OTC Collections	Payment as a % of Patients' Balances	Percentage of Patients that Paid the Visit Co-Pay
Historical performance	$1,175	12	55
30-day target		50	80
60-day target		70	100
90-day target		90	100

OTC = over-the-counter.

come obstacles that prevent this. At the same time, recognize that not every employee is right for this position. Some people just can't get comfortable asking patients for money. Know when you need to shift a different person into the position before someone feels inadequate or thinks he or she has failed.

ACCOUNTS RECEIVABLE MANAGEMENT

Examine A/R indicators to identify red flags, and know when it's time to dig deeper to correct underlying problems and get the money collected. There are a few benchmarks that should be looked at each month. When the practice doesn't fall within the norm, start digging. The benchmarks vary by specialty, but these general benchmarks provide a good starting point for evaluating A/R performance:

- Total A/R less than two times monthly charges;
- Less than 15% of total receivables aged at 120 days or older; and
- Collection ratio of 95% of adjusted charges (adjusted charges are calculated by subtracting contractual adjustments from the monthly charges).

Third-Party Reimbursement Analysis

Develop a procedure for spot-checking EOBs to be sure the insurance plan paid the claim correctly and the billing department properly audited the claim and made the appropriate contractual adjustment. Errors in this process can be very costly to the practice. I've seen as much as $200,000 inappropriately adjusted off accounts because employees assumed the insurance company paid the right fee for each service. There was one situation where the billing department was reading Medicare EOBs incorrectly and wrote off the 20% patient responsibility, amounting to $83,000 in one year. Give the responsibility for auditing claims the attention it deserves! Properly train employees and monitor outcomes.

The EOB also reports denied payment for a service. Be sure the staff appeals these claims when warranted. If the denial is a result of coding errors, it's important to inform the providers and show them how to properly code the service in the future.

Where's the Money?

If the A/R more than 120-days old rises above the norm, run a report on aging by payer class. This will identify a potential troublesome payer. The administrator can then take quick action to recover the money. The out-of-norm aging could be the result of claims kicked back to the practice with errors, or claims might be stockpiled on the desk of someone at the insurance plan. It might even be an indication that the insurance plan has financial trouble causing it to stall payments. The faster you take action, the better the chance of collecting the revenue.

There might also be large patient balances driving up the aged receivables. Perhaps the practice is keeping "dead wood" on the books. If accounts are uncollectible, the sooner they are turned over to a collection agency, the better the chance of recovery. If the practice has not received payment after four months of sending patient statements, send the account out to a collection agency and write it off the books. However, when this happens, it's time to tighten the financial policies on patient responsibility and improve collection procedures:

1. Telephone patients for payment when a second statement does not result in payment. Phone calls are far more effective than patient statements, which are silent.
2. Critique the patient statements. Are they easy to understand, and do they clearly show the patient what is owed?
3. Review the current dunning messages. Perhaps the messages need to be progressively stronger to get the patient's attention.
4. Consider a pre-collection letter-writing service, such as Transworld Systems, to boost patient collections. This will speed up the process and reduce time spent by staff chasing the money. Often, the patient will respond better to a third party—taking the demand for payment more seriously—resulting in prompt resolution of the debt.

Patient collections are one of the most challenging responsibilities in the office, and sometimes the staff needs a little motivation. Setting collection target goals and offering incentives to collectors may improve the practice's performance in this area. With employers passing more of the financial responsibility for medical care to patients, physicians and administrators need to pay close attention to how well this aspect of collections is managed.

REAL-TIME CLAIMS ADJUDICATION

Most of us on the business side of medicine have been frustrated at the challenges of understanding the patients' insurance coverage and their personal responsibility for the visit. How many times have you thought, "When I go to a retail store, they scan my credit card when the transaction occurs and immediately know whether they will get paid. Why can't we do that in the medical facility?" Well, that day may be on the horizon with real-time claims adjudication (RTCA) plans under development in the payer industry.

RTCA will change the way we do business in the front office and in the billing department. Payer payment expectations will be verified at the time the service is rendered—and that is exciting news for medical practices, dental practices and ambulatory care centers.

With RTCA, when the patient is seen for a visit and the charges are posted, those charges produce an EOB while the patient is still in the office. The insurance plan adjudicates the claim in real-time and electronically informs the practice of what the payment will be. This means the practice will know what the insurance payment should be so that it can collect the patient's payment for his or her share of costs before the patient leaves the office. The payer's payment will be deposited electronically into the practice's bank account within a specified amount of time. Look at these potential advantages:

- Improved cash flow;
- Minimal follow-up on claims;
- Greatly reduced number of patient statements;
- Minimal follow-up on patient balances;
- Improved consistency;
- Increased efficiency and reduced errors; and
- Reduced number of staff processes due to all of these improvements.

For several years, a number of larger insurance companies have been working with bigger practices to beta test the implementation of the RTCA system and refine the processes involved before it goes to the broader market. It is slowly moving toward realization for all practices, hopefully in the near future.

Inevitably, this will change the entire make-up of the front office and billing staff. Selected members of the insurance staff will move from the back office to the front office and handle the exit process with the patients. The staffer/patient review of the RTCA of a specific patient encounter is expected to trigger the following processes:

1. Identifying if insurance information collected from the patient is accurate and coverage is valid;
2. Reviewing the daily charges and verifying RTCA insurance payment;

3. Collecting the patient's entire portion for the visit, based on the payer's RTCA; and

4. Reducing staffing needs.

This will result in drastically reducing the number of processes and the time that typically has been involved in monitoring open claims. It will further reduce the number of hours and staffing costs required to:

- Submit claims tracers;
- Send patient statements and request payment; and
- Perform collection processes.

RTCA is revolutionary and is expected to have a positive impact on practice finances by improving cash flow, improving office efficiency, improving consistency and reducing process errors and staffing needs, which inevitably will reduce practice overhead. The RTCA system will go a long way toward improving communication about finances and patients' responsibility for the services that are rendered, which will result in better patient services; elimination of confusion about what is expected of patients financially; and a clearer understanding by patients of the practice's expectation of getting paid when services are rendered.

WHOSE PRACTICE IS IT, ANYWAY?

Beginning with contracting and ending with collections and making sure the payments get to the bank, every decision and step along the way influence the ability to get paid for what you do and how well practice finances are protected. Physicians need to assume responsibility for these decisions and take back the control of practice finances. Sometimes that means learning to say NO.

When you aren't satisfied, do something about it! If it's a payer problem, go back to the drawing board to negotiate and agree on revised contract terms. If the situation warrants it, fire the payer. If it's a staff training or performance issue, address it. Give staff members the tools to do their job and hold them accountable.

DON'T BE A TARGET FOR EMBEZZLEMENT

Poor financial record keeping and blind trust are invitations for embezzlement. Most physicians and administrators know someone that has been a victim of a financial scam to embezzle from a medical practice. Embezzlement is an orchestrated illegal plan to part you from your money without your knowledge.

The clever embezzler lures his victim into a false sense of security and complacency, gains trust and then tests the waters. If he gets away with it (and they usually do), he becomes confident and continues the scam.

Don't be the culprit of an embezzlement scheme that has your practice financing someone else's vacation home or kids' college education. Do what it takes to protect the practice revenue, and get the practice in "protective financial order."

Take Financial Notice

I have observed a number of practices where finances are handled casually: cash loosely kept in drawers and not reconciled to practice records before it hits the bank deposit, bank statements looked at only by the office bookkeeper, the computer system with a poor audit trail, no policy or oversight for adjustments on patient accounts and payroll records not scrutinized. On the physicians' part, this casual response to handling finances may be neglect or perhaps "too much" trust. Either way, it provides an opportunity for embezzlement and may, in fact, encourage it.

Embezzlement can occur at many locations throughout the office. It can be at the front desk, the insurance department, payroll or the accounts payable. But it almost always starts small. It can begin by the perpetrator borrowing $20 from the cash drawer for lunch, but if it doesn't get repaid and goes unnoticed, the waters have been tested. The thief now has "permission" to take the next step.

Separation of Duties

Efficiency of a medical office depends on streamlining procedures and avoiding duplication of tasks. At the same time, multiple people need to be involved in finances, creating a separation of duties. Don't have one person audit the cash drawer, post the charge and payment and take the money to the bank. It's important that the person who prepares the checks is not the same one that reconciles the bank statement.

Create essential financial-role diversity by requiring anyone handling finances to rotate out of the position for a period of at least two consecutive weeks each year. If someone has something to hide, she sure doesn't want someone else doing her job for two weeks. This discourages the thief, but it's not foolproof. Clever employees can sometimes find ways to outsmart the system or clean up their act during the weeks preceding their time off. They are deceptive and will do what it takes to avoid discovery.

Beyond having multiple people involved in financial transactions, it is equally important to have processes that ensure clear and appropriate documentation to support all financial transactions—money in and money out. This documentation serves as the audit trail. It allows the practice to spot-check, ensuring the financial processes are being adhered to. This is one case where duplication of effort is a powerful financial tool.

Looking over someone's shoulder occasionally helps keep him honest. In a small practice, the doctor or an independent source such as the accountant or consultant can be the point person for accountability. A larger practice may use an independent source or have an audit committee composed of employees from various departments. Administrators and physicians need to make periodic financial reviews and audits a priority. Here are 12 simple rules you can put in place that will go a long way toward protecting practice finances:

1. Use an automated check-writing system that prints checks and leaves no room for alteration.
2. Have a bank lockbox for receiving all mail in payments on patient accounts.
3. Audit the cash drawer daily.
4. Never borrow from the cash box (or others will).
5. Eliminate signature stamps with the same names as the signers on bank accounts.
6. Have bank statements come to the home of one of the physicians, and have someone that neither writes the checks nor makes the bank deposits complete the reconciliation.
7. If a nonowner of the practice is permitted to be a signer on the bank account, limit the dollar amount approved.
8. Audit payroll records semi-annually for unauthorized raises, bonuses or overtime pay.
9. Conduct reference checks on all potential employees before you hire them.
10. Purchase insurance bonds on employees that handle money, but keep in mind this does not cover neglect.
11. Spot-check financial transactions and records, including adjustments on patient accounts.
12. Listen to your instincts. If you become suspicious, start digging.

Establish strong financial safeguards for the practice and adhere to them. It's a matter of sound business principles and a prudent way to conduct business. Existing employees will appreciate a solid foundation and a clear understanding of how things need to be done. New hires will recognize the practice's respect for finances and know what is expected of them. They will understand this practice "minds the store."

Communicate Consequences

As a final note, during each employee's orientation discuss the financial principles of the practice and let the new employee know you will not tolerate deceit, fraud or theft. Too many practices leave financial matters unspoken, and too many physicians that have been the victim of embezzlement fail to prosecute. Let your staff know you would!

THE SECRETS

1. Getting paid for what you do begins with contracting issues.
2. Scrutinize contracts and make your own contracting decisions.
3. Conduct internal chart audits.
4. Look at E&M coding patterns.
5. Monitor charge entry, claims submission and payment-timing trends.
6. Audit contract payments and adjustments for accuracy.
7. Know when to terminate a payer.
8. Establish standards for managing revenue processes.
9. Keep in mind that patients will assume more financial responsibility for medical care in the future.
10. Tighten procedures and controls for patient financial responsibility, including OTC payments.
11. Take charge of practice finances, and hold people accountable.
12. Take proactive steps to avoid embezzlement.

FORM ADDED TO YOUR TOOLBOX:

☞ *Payer Performance Table*

CHAPTER 10

Great Employees— The Simple Truth!

W hat hasn't been said or written about the difficulty in managing human resources (HR)? When HR troubles rise to the top of management's concerns, they can encompass a menagerie of problems: turnover, overtime, poor attendance, poor attitude, low productivity, lack of respect—you name it! It's all about people; what they bring to and how they feel about the workplace. When it's not working, there are major headaches.

KEY FACT: *When employees believe they work "with" the practice, rather than "for" the practice, they become an intricate part of the practice's success.*

Everyone is searching for the best employees. You look for ways to improve your recruitment efforts through better screening tools and testing instruments. You hone your interview skills and improve your analysis of applicants. In the end, it's a gamble and just a matter of improving your odds.

While it's not easy to find peak-performing employees, the poor performers surely will make their presence felt. You know the old 80/20 rule: you spend 80% of your time dealing with 20% of the people. Most often, unfortunately, the problem employees get the attention, and sometimes this investment of management's time doesn't pay off. The top-performing, dedicated employees are worthy of our time—the ones we'd like to clone. The great ones! So what are the secrets to making a great employee? How do you turn ordinary people into great employees? I'm about to tell you the simple truths I've learned.

The best employees are not molded by the technical skills managers apply. The best employees are not created by the things taught in the HR classes you took in college. The best employees are not created through rigorous academic analysis or through textbook applications. These tools are useful in helping understand employees and discovering ways to approach HR management, but they are not at the core of what makes great employees.

LOOK AT ROBIN

Take Robin, for example. Robin worked with Las Posas Family Practice, a five-physician medical group, for more than 10 years. Notice I said she worked *with* the practice and not *for* the practice. There's a big difference. Working for a practice is doing a job. Working with the practice is being an intricate part of the business—taking responsibility for what you do and pride in what you accomplish for the practice. That's Robin!

Providing and Taking Opportunity

Robin started working with Las Posas Family Practice when she was a college student. She worked her way up from file clerk to managing the billing department. Robin was thirsty for knowledge, taking every opportunity to learn more and expand her skills. The physicians and manager of this practice, by the same token, recognized Robin's potential and opened up the doors of opportunity. Everyone benefited. Robin gained confidence and knew she was valued. Management could depend on Robin whenever she was called on to learn a new task or assume more responsibility. She became the model employee.

Character Counts

We all know character plays a vital role in the value of an employee and his or her contribution in the workplace. Robin is a perfect example. She is dedicated, honest, dependable, flexible, open-minded and sincere. These are character traits that start you on the road to building a great employee. Let's look at what these character traits do for business performance and professional growth:

- Dedicated employees are loyal and represent the practice in a favorable manner. They take their job seriously, and it shows in their performance.
- Honest employees have better attendance—management and coworkers can depend on them. They are considerate and respectful of superiors and peers.
- Employees that are flexible and open-minded become excellent team players. They adapt to a changing environment and pitch in when other workers need a hand. They learn how to solve problems and how to help

other people solve problems. They are quick to find a more-efficient way to get something done and are sincere in their interactions with patients, staff and management.

These character traits are the core of what becomes a model employee. While you should try to hire those with desirable character traits, management's ideals, attitudes and actions largely determine if the employee excels.

People with questionable character traits simply aren't going to become great employees. Good managers can strengthen the character of staff if there's a solid foundation, but building character is not your job. If you focus on building character into employees, you will be falling victim to the old 80/20 rule. You will spend endless hours trying to shape employees who, in the end, are not going to make the same investment in the practice—and don't discount the possible negative impact on the rest of the staff. Don't alienate staff or waste your time. Naturally, problem employees often require some meaningful attention, but spend the bulk of your time where you'll reap a better return on your investment.

Believe in Your Heart

Believing in your heart isn't meant to sound soft or sentimental. Physicians and administrators at the helm of a great practice are instrumental in creating a culture that tells employees they are valued. To create great employees, you must believe in your heart that they can excel and be great at what they do.

Take Robin. When I asked her what was great about her job at Las Posas Family Practice, she brightened up and couldn't stop talking. She told how she was just a college student when she came to work at Las Posas and how they gave her a chance. They worked around her hours, and when they moved her from file clerk to receptionist they believed she could do the job at a time when she wasn't quite so sure. They encouraged her, giving her more responsibility and more support. She said the doctors had a "can do" attitude, always believing in and encouraging staff.

Robin told me how her confidence grew and that everything she achieved at Las Posas was because the physicians believed in her. She told me how respectful and caring they were to the patients and staff. They gave her extra time off and were truly sympathetic when a family emergency occurred. She talked about the terrific Christmas parties, always hosted by one of the physicians in his home. The physicians at Las Posas Family Practice created a wonderful culture, and demonstrated how much they valued Robin—they believed in her ability in their hearts.

Take Susan—the "Perfect Receptionist" in Chapter 2. She certainly understands the value she brings to the practice. She knows she has an important job and that management will provide her with whatever support she needs. Susan has confidence, feels appreciated and loves her job. Employees only feel this way when management is sincere and recognizes their value and that their contribution is part of management's own success! Management leads the way in making the difference between mediocre and great employees.

GET OFF TO A GOOD START

Wouldn't it be wonderful if at the end of the first day on the new job every employee went home feeling like they had the perfect job and a great employer? With a little effort and a big commitment, you have the ability to make new employees feel that working for you is one of the best decisions they ever made.

It starts with first impressions and what you do to develop a positive experience for the new employee. Ask Laura Sachs Hills, the author of *How to Recruit, Motivate, and Manage a Winning Staff*, a fantastic how-to book (Greenbranch Publishing, 2004). Laura says, "With a little planning and effort, the new employee can have a positive start and quickly become a motivated and productive member of your team." Laura is right, it's up to you. You hold all the cards in your hand.

Here are a few of her ideas on how to integrate new employees into the practice and give them the sense that they belong from day one:

1. Plan ahead and provide the essentials. This includes clearing the employee's workspace—desk, cabinets, bulletin board, telephone, etc. Make sure the space is clean and stocked with fresh supplies and properly functioning equipment. Remove personal items left by former employees.
2. Engrave a nametag for the new employee and a desk or office-door sign with his or her name and title, if appropriate.
3. Introduce the new employee to each member of your staff. Explain each person's responsibilities and job duties. If the employee will be supervised by your office or clinical manager, or another person, introduce him or her.

4. Outline what the new employee is to do that day and throughout the orientation period. Prepare a checklist of all the tasks to be learned and who in your office will do the training. Choose trainers who have mastered the task and who are willing and capable teachers.

5. Give the new employee a guided tour of the office. Point out the staff restroom, coat/storage closet, and break room.

6. Capture your new employee's debut on film. The day will come when you introduce a new employee to his or her first patient. This is a big moment for many new employees and particularly for new associates fresh out of school. Don't let this moment come and go unnoticed.

7. Assign one staff member the task of being the new employee's "buddy." He or she will serve as your new employee's mentor and troubleshooter.

Here are a few of my own ideas to add to the list:

1. Prepare a brief biographical sketch of the employee to include on a welcome flyer with his photo. Include a little about his professional background, but personal information is even more important. State how long he has lived in the community, tell a little about his family, favorite hobbies, food and perhaps his favorite vacation, sports team or whatever. Pass a copy out to each employee before the new employee starts.

2. Introduce the new employee to patients by enlarging the biographical flyer onto poster board that is placed on an easel in the reception room. Add a header "Meet our latest addition!"

3. Provide the employee with a fact sheet about the practice. This should include the names of each physician and when he or she first entered the practice, a list of employees including their titles and phone extension, the practice's philosophy and mission statement and answers to the 10 most common questions patients ask.

4. Have a staff luncheon in honor of the employee during the first week of employment.

5. Have the new employee's immediate supervisor meet with him at the end of each day during the first week or so. Answer questions, and give the new employee encouragement or support as needed.

6. Take a photo of the new employee on the first day of work and have it enlarged for the staff bulletin board. Take some additional "at work" photos (during the first month) that can be added to the practice's photo album/scrapbook. Circulate the scrapbook at the next staff meeting.

Why is all this effort dedicated to a new employee so important? In the words of Laura Sachs Hills, "What you do from the moment your new employee steps into your office can determine whether she becomes an asset or a liability. Just a little bit of extra attention to this critical time can reduce your turnover and speed the new employee's acclimation to your practice." I couldn't agree more. This up-front investment you make sends the new employee a strong message about his new workplace and how you treat and value employees.

THE VISIBLE MANAGER

Managers and physicians have awesome responsibilities. Sometimes there is just so much to do in a day, a week, a month that they are easily buried in administrative and clinical responsibilities. This can, unintentionally, leave little time dedicated to staff and staff responsibilities. Unfortunately, this often results in staff feeling that the doctors and managers are unapproachable. It can even cause employees to feel like their problems are too small to bring to their supervisor's attention. When this occurs, a wall forms between management and staff that can be troublesome.

If staff members do not feel comfortable going to managers, they will begin making decisions on their own that they are neither authorized nor equipped to make. They may muddle their way through a problem hoping to solve it without their supervisor ever knowing about it. This breakdown in communication sometimes compromises the end result of the very problem they are trying to fix. Staff members may feel they don't have the support needed to do the job right. Be sensitive to the nonverbal messages your actions (or failure to act) send to employees.

No matter how busy you are, it's important to walk the floor and circulate. When you mingle with employees while they are working, you not only connect with them, you also learn about their work processes as well as problems and areas of the practice that are changing. For example, you may see patient bottlenecks at the exit station that didn't used to exist. What has caused this change? Is it because Jennifer can't keep up since she has taken on more tasks? Has the computer slowed down? Are there more patients? You may see other situations that are worthy of your attention— like a mound of filing stacked up in the medical records department.

Talk to the employees: see what they are doing and what they need. Find out what difficulties they confront and give encouragement and praise.

Your visibility demonstrates the commitment to your staff members and interest in the challenges they face each day.

How approachable are you?

- Are you the physician that walks in the back door and either heads for your office or immediately starts seeing patients without acknowledging the staff, or are you the physician that greets everyone and pays special attention to new employees?
- Are you the physician that skips out of staff meetings because you have something more important to do, or are you the one that knows the meeting is an opportunity to connect with staff members and find out what's on their minds?
- Are you the administrator that is squirreled away in your office going over important reports and meeting with decision makers, or are you the administrator that carves out time each day to survey the office to see how staff is doing and give your support?
- Are you the practice executive that meets with staff members only when you need to reprimand them, or are you the special manager that calls someone into your office for a little encouragement or praise?
- Are you the manager that puts off performance reviews because they are a nuisance and take up so much time, or do you schedule these reviews when they are due because you recognize reviews are an opportunity to connect with employees, offer constructive criticism, acknowledge achievements and guide good employees on the road to becoming great employees?

If you want the best from your employees, create a united front and show your appreciation—be there, be visible.

OPEN COMMUNICATION

Open communication means *exchanging* information—speaking and listening. Open communication allows people to speak freely and honestly to understand another's point of view. That's a powerful tool. Sometimes spontaneous communication is best. In other words, if someone has something on her mind and is given the opportunity to talk about it, each of you will understand the other and will not be left to form erroneous opinions. When managers are available and encourage employees to come to them with concerns, they can detect problems, nip them in the bud and encourage further communication and problem solving.

How do you encourage open communication? Begin with setting a communication policy whereby employees go first to their supervisor with problems, rather than bypassing this level and going to the practice administrator or a physician to get questions answered and problems solved. Managers and physicians should reinforce this policy. This policy should hold for both business and clinical staff. There is sometimes a tendency for clinical staff members to go directly to the doctors rather than their supervisors. Doctors need to discourage such actions.

Next, establish times when you are available to employees. Since the first few hours of the morning yield the highest production if uninterrupted, allow employees to come into your office between 11:00 AM and 12:30 PM each day and again during the last hour of the day. With this type of schedule, you are available to discuss major issues; but employees won't be able to immediately come to you with minor problems, so they may be more inclined to resolve these types of problems on their own.

Take Time to Connect

If you are in charge of an office large enough to have managers for each department, you may want to have management huddles for a half-hour each day or weekly brown-bag lunch meetings. In a smaller office, a morning huddle with the entire staff can be an excellent way to start the day. Such investments of time help everyone plan their day and head off minor problems before they erupt into something bigger.

Regular staff meetings allow for interoffice and interdepartmental communication and exchange of ideas. They also are an opportunity to discuss policy and procedural changes and announce activities that are in the practice pipeline. When information is relayed at a staff meeting, everyone hears the same thing at the same time, eliminating room for miscommunication. Staff meetings also encourage open dialogue, allowing for clarification and a chance for staff members to state their opinions or offer suggestions. This is a far-more-effective method to inform staff than relaying information through appointed messengers. The "grapevine" approach results in misinterpretation or failure to fully communicate the same information to everyone.

Rules of meetings include planning, creating and following a prepared agenda, staying on time, encouraging the entire staff to participate and documenting action items with a target date and who is assigned to handle the task. Reinforce the importance of meetings by not canceling them unless absolutely necessary and not reacting to trivial office circumstances by calling unnecessary meetings that disrupt workflow and interfere with maintaining a calm and productive environment.

Memos are an important way to communicate time-sensitive information between meetings. Memos can be distributed by posting on a bulletin board, hand-delivering hard copies or sending electronically through interoffice email. Whatever form you choose, it's important that all employees get their copy in the same time frame. If one person is left out of the loop, the communication breakdown can be damaging. A word of caution on the use of memos: Do not use memos to avoid open dialogue as this can cause staff resentment. Memos cannot replace one-on-one communication or meetings with open discussion.

One-on-one meetings should be considered unique events. If they happen too often, they lose their importance. If they are scheduled too infrequently, you are not connecting with individuals that you value. One-on-one meetings are best when regarded as special—the annual performance review, the announcement of a promotion and the occasional time you simply call someone in to tell him he is doing a good job and to keep up the good work. Hopefully, this communication inspires people to give their best, resulting in less need to call people in because their performance is deteriorating. However, such meetings are occasionally necessary, and it's vitally important that any employee criticism be done in private. Remember the saying, "praise in public, criticize in private." Public criticism is devastating to morale and shows a lack of respect for staff.

MAKE EVERYONE A WINNER

Develop a culture that inspires staff members to do their best. This ongoing process starts at the top. There are a number of ways a practice develops a culture that empowers staff to be productive and enrich the practice. The skillful manager develops a relationship with each individual member of the staff to better understand what each person needs and wants from the job. Beyond the obvious advantage of feeling a sense of belonging, what motivates Melissa may not be what motivates Tom. Get to know your employees and how you can contribute to their success. Think outside the box and be creative.

Giving to Employees

There are many ways the practice can give more to its employees, and it's not always a financial investment. This is why it is essential to understand what motivates your employees and to recognize their broader needs. There is a multitude of ways to invest in staff members and make them feel important. With a little thought and creativity you can give them what they need and will appreciate—something that is mutually beneficial.

For example, young mothers that work might prefer working part-time around their children's school hours to avoid paying for childcare that would take a big chunk of their paycheck. Some employees like flexible schedules or job sharing. These are things you can offer that don't add to your staffing costs, but go a long way in recognizing the needs of employees and gaining their loyalty. And when it comes to job sharing and part-time workers, these are the employees you can count on when someone is on vacation or out sick. These employees are the ones that provide needed support when workloads fluctuate or the practice experiences temporary demands such as a computer conversion, opening a satellite office or bringing a new doctor on board.

On the other hand, you may have several employees that are taking college courses at night. Giving a $100 book stipend each semester is a wonderful way to honor your employees' dedication to furthering their education. Your investment can provide job enrichment and rewards for employees. Take the medical assistant that wants to return to school and obtain her RN. There are many ways to support her effort. Perhaps you might offer to move her to part time so she can attend classes two afternoons each week, or you might commit to pay a percentage of the costs for her schooling and/or giving her a one-time bonus if she stays on with the practice for a stated length of time after she becomes registered.

Perhaps you have an employee that has his limited x-ray license but aspires to be a magnetic resonance imaging (MRI) technician. This might be the opportunity to explore his desires and match them to your needs. Maybe the number of MRIs the practice is referring out justifies bringing this service in house. If so, establishing a time line that brings MRI aboard at the same time this employee is finishing his training would be mutually beneficial.

Send employees (at your expense and on the practice's clock) to workshops and seminars that enhance their on-the-job skills and keep them current in their field. Don't limit training to clinical courses or coding. All employees need to hone their skills from time to time. A day out of the office with peers from other practices can be energizing, and employees will return with tips to help them on the job. Job enrichment is an important element in obtaining peak performance. You can emphasize employee value while boosting their confidence by having employees share what they learned at the next staff meeting.

Be a Joiner

Ask your staff to participate in professional organizations, and have the practice pay the fees. For management staff, there is the Professional Association of Health Care Office Management (PAHCOM; www.pahcom.com) and the Medical Group Management Association (MGMA; www.mgma.com), both of which have certification programs that help their members expand their knowledge base and obtain recognition for it. What they learn through certification programs, conferences or workshops will apply to their job.

There are also specialty organizations for other positions in the practice. You may want your head nurse to belong to the National Association of Healthcare Quality (www.nahq.org), and your coder can become certified with the American Academy of Professional Coders (www.aapc.com). This all makes for stronger staff and a stronger practice. Employees are one of your greatest assets—let your actions show how you value them!

Coaching

Coaching is a matter of creating a climate where everyone wins. The attention you give to employees and the attention every member of the team gives to each other is the yardstick for measuring your success as captain of the team. It's unrealistic to expect that each employee will become great, but if all members of the team are performing at close to their potential, you have achieved the goal of the coach. And if we continually raise the bar on our expectations for group performance, individual performance also rises.

Management must fulfill its promises to staff and remain steadfast in defining and communicating goals. Everyone must be held to the same high standard. If Krista at the front desk is expected to be on time every morning, Jason in billing should be expected to be on time as well. Your policies and actions must reflect a commitment to consistency and fairness.

Here's a simple way to check your consistency with your team members. Create a list composed of three columns labeled "Great," "Good" and "Poor." Classify each employee under one of these columns. Now pull the HR files and compare each person's last performance review with the category you gave him or her. If it doesn't match, inconsistencies exist in the standards you maintain for staff. To improve the performance of average and low performers, you must expect them to meet predetermined standards evenly applied across the board. They need to know you have expectations you will hold them to. Meanwhile, don't forget that constructive criticism and encouragement are essential to improving the outcome.

Your top-performing employees need attention and recognition as well. The visible manager understands that everyone needs appreciation, support and reassurance from time to time.

About the Money

People work for reasons other than money, although money certainly plays an important role. It has been my experience that employees with a job they enjoy and a practice they feel truly involved in don't leave for an extra dollar an hour. That being said, pay people what they are worth!

The amount of education, experience and job responsibilities should dictate the variance between one position and another in weighting the pay rate. For example, there would be a natural differential between the receptionist and the billing supervisor's job requirements and pay rate. Develop job descriptions that define the criteria for each position, and weight the base of pay accordingly. Once you have established a weight, the traditional pay rates for your geographic area will dictate the supply-and-demand aspects that influence pay scales.

Gather information from local and national sources regarding pay rates to use as a baseline. Check with your chamber of commerce, employment agencies, the local medical society and other medical practices to find out what the "going rate" is. Statistical information on salaries specifically for health care professionals is also available through MGMA, PAHCOM and the Health Care Group (www.healthcaregroup.com).

Setting wages is not the place to skimp. Employers that pay in the top 20% of the area's medical practices generally do so because their employees are worth it. Pay staff fairly, but don't pay more than you should. I've seen practices where two employees sit side-by-side, with the same skills, doing the same job, and the new employee is making 30% more than the other. This is not reasonable or fair. Problems occur when you don't establish salary ranges for each position and stick with them. It happens when we are interviewing and make an emotional decision to hire someone asking for a pay rate that doesn't fit with the existing job requirements and responsibilities. The candidate may have been paid more in her last position because she assumed more responsibilities or lived in an area where salaries are traditionally higher. Don't be enticed by demands for a higher salary. Take this opportunity to inform the applicant by reviewing the job description, discussing how you arrived at the salary range for the position and explaining why you cannot go beyond the structured range to hire her.

NO-TOLERANCE POLICY

Turn the old 80/20 rule on its heels. You don't have 80% of your time to dedicate to the poor performer, so don't do it. You know the poor employee—the one who doesn't want to do his fair share of the work, is irresponsible or has a bad attitude. It's easy to detect. Sometimes we avoid dealing with the poor performer in hopes that things will get better. Face the music—in most cases improvement is not likely.

When performance is slipping, give the person an opportunity to improve, but hold to your high standards. Don't waiver. Even though the employee may have great skills for the job, if he isn't committed or simply doesn't fit in your practice it's best to deal with it sooner rather than later. Besides, there's the "poisoned well" syndrome. It doesn't take long for the employee with a bad attitude to get things brewing among the staff. Morale will quickly deteriorate unless you develop a no-tolerance policy.

Performance issues require a tiered approach to resolution. You know the script. First is the verbal warning or counseling session, followed by a formal write-up and disciplinary action and finally resolution—satisfactory performance or termination. I am surprised by how many times some practices stall in the second tier. The employees are warned, but the situation is never resolved. Sometimes these practices give repeated warnings, but fail to terminate—in effect giving employees permission to continue their offending actions. It is unfair to those employees that do their job, and it compromises the practice's overall performance.

When employees are given a written warning, the expected result must be defined objectively with a specific time frame. If this goal is not met, management has the responsibility to terminate the employees.

When it becomes necessary to discharge an employee, do it with dignity. Make it brief, and give the specific reasons, but also tell him about his good points. Suggest the type of position he might pursue that more suitably matches his skills and personality traits.

YOUR #1 CUSTOMER

If you remember that employees are your first customers, you can't go wrong. Their needs and desires vary with time, as their personal lives evolve and the work environment changes. To keep tabs on whether you are on target with meeting their needs, periodically conduct an anonymous staff survey that rates management—preferably conducted by someone outside the practice, such as the accountant or practice management consultant.

Also conduct exit interviews with each staff member that resigns. Don't do this on her last day, but perhaps a week before she departs. Use this opportunity for her to critique management and provide constructive suggestions. Departing employees have a tendency to say everything is fine, so ask open-ended questions that call for more than a yes-or-no answer such as, "Sherri, you have been in our medical records department for three years. What changes have occurred during that time and how have they impacted your job?" "What could we have done to make your job easier?" "What task did you like least about your job (and why)?"

The survey and interview results can guide your efforts to keep employees motivated and productive. Managing HR is an ongoing and changing process, as you deal with different generations of staff with different expectations. Polling staff from time to time helps you understand these differences and respond accordingly.

THE FAST TRACK TO LEADERSHIP

In my work as a consultant and speaker, I have the opportunity to meet hundreds of physicians and practice leaders each year. These leaders are CEOs, practice administrators, office managers, chiefs of clinical operations and a myriad of other titles with equally diverse responsibilities and achievements. It is a privilege to learn more about these people and to understand both their challenges and accomplishments. Occasionally I meet someone that is very special—so special that I remember the individual long after we meet. Amanda Wood, the Director of Clinical Operations of an ear, nose and throat (ENT) practice in Oklahoma, is one of those people, and you are about to learn why.

Career Start

Amanda has worked her way up the organizational ladder. She took her first position in healthcare in 2002 at the age of 22. She was hired as a front desk receptionist for Oklahoma Otolaryngology Associates, P.C. It was then a five-physician practice with two locations within the Oklahoma City metropolitan area. Otolaryngology Associates provides general ENT services, audiology and allergy care for a diverse age group ranging from pediatrics to geriatrics.

Amanda worked in this full-time position for a year and a half before requesting relocation to the north Oklahoma City location.

She became the head receptionist and advanced to Lead Supervisor in late 2003—quite an accomplishment in such a short period of time. Amanda was supervising mature receptionists with far more experience than she had, and she found it to be a little intimidating. At first she felt insecure, but soon became more comfortable and earned the respect of the staff she supervised. This position required a fast learning curve, and Amanda had to understand the job quickly since the person she replaced was not there to provide guidance or direction. At the time, there were no training tools in place for her to refer to.

It didn't take long for Amanda to figure things out, and before long she was developing training tools for her department. She created a front desk "How To" training manual that describes every step from beginning to end for each job description. This helps employees understand their responsibilities and is a reference tool for how each task should be performed. Amanda also updated the policies and procedures manual for the front desk.

Amanda received another promotion and became the Operations Coordinator, reporting directly to the Chief Operations Officer. Amanda thrived in an environment that allowed her to continually increase her skills and reach new levels of achievement. She willingly accepted the responsibility that came with each position and was appointed Director of Clinical Operations in 2004, reporting directly to the President of the physician board.

Practice Growth

Since that time, Amanda has made some significant contributions to the organization, including recruiting and hiring three physicians and assuming all the challenges and responsibilities of opening a third office in Edmond, Oklahoma, in 2007. And in 2009, she was the Program Chair for one of her national management affiliations, The Association of Otolaryngology Administrators.

Valuing Staff

When I met Amanda (who has since married and is now Amanda Wood-Foutch), I was surprised to discover how much she had accomplished in only seven years. What struck me the most about Amanda was not these achievements, although they are quite impressive, but rather it was her humility and what she values most that were extraordinary.

I simply had to ask her what she was the most proud of. Her answer surprised me and may surprise you. It is a testament to the kind of leader she is and the culture she works in. She thought carefully for a few minutes and then said with enthusiasm: "The thing I take the greatest pride in is the fact that the very first person I hired is still with us." That is more than humble; it is the very core of why she is so successful at such a young age. That first hire was a medical assistant named Tia Gentry. Tia has grown professionally and is now the Clinical Team Lead for the Norman office.

This is a wonderful example of what happens when you value staff members and don't put management above them. Employees that are nurtured and encouraged become more confident, productive and loyal. Some of them become great.

Being an effective leader requires a combination of skill, art, instinct and respect. People achieve their best when you expect a lot from them, as long as you give a lot back and are consistently honest and fair. In essence, the simple truths all add up to treating people right!

THE SECRETS

1. Make employees feel valuable.
2. Provide opportunity for growth, and staff will have a vested interest in the practice.
3. Top employees start with strong character traits.
4. Express confidence in staff, and they will become confident.

5. Invest in the right employees.
6. Loyalty comes from "believing" in employees.
7. Recognize and praise individual talents.
8. Be approachable and visible every day.
9. Develop a no-tolerance policy for poor performance.

FORMS ADDED TO YOUR TOOLBOX:

↪ *Sample Bio Sketch*
↪ *Meeting Action Matrix*
↪ *Staff Survey: How Does Management Rate?*
↪ *Management Skills Audit*

CHAPTER 11

The Money Crunch

"We have a cash flow crisis and don't know how to fix it!" These were the words of Marci Bradford, M.D., the senior doctor of Evergreen Women's Center when she called my office. Despite a high demand for its services, the practice was struggling with finances, and the physicians were in a panic. The practice was financed to the max and not prepared to handle further financial obligations.

KEY FACT: *Planning for the future and monitoring progress are critical components to successful growth and financial management.*

Evergreen's financial woes were felt throughout the organization, creating quite a stir. No one was monitoring the income and expense trends, and there was never enough money to pay the bills. Through the grapevine, staff members heard about the money problems, and they were feeling uneasy. After a couple of payroll checks bounced, some of the staff began to bail. The stability and future of the practice were in question.

THEY GREW TOO FAST

I soon learned that Evergreen Women's Center was a victim of its own success. The center was started by Dr. Bradford three years prior and appeared to be an immediate success, adding two more physicians within the first year. By the end of the second year, Evergreen hired two nurse practitioners.

Dr. Bradford was planning to offer a partnership to the other physicians, but had to get the finances in order first. With the current state of affairs, this wasn't possible, and physician confidence in the practice was waning. This was a major concern for Dr. Bradford.

Evergreen Women's Center couldn't get a handle on its growth or practice finances. It took money to expand a practice and meet patient demand, but seeing more patients wasn't providing the revenue required to meet financial obligations. Dr. Bradford recently secured a lease on a second office, but Evergreen's current financial situation prevented it from equipping and opening the office. The practice was about to recruit a fourth physician when Dr. Bradford put on the brakes and called me.

In addition to the typical operating expenses, there were financial obligations for capital investment. More capital expenditures were on the horizon for the new office, and Evergreen was about to borrow more money just to keep it afloat. Evergreen needed a financial-recovery plan and needed it fast.

CHECKING OUT THE NUMBERS

In order to give Evergreen the help it sought, it was critical for me to get a clear understanding of the financial picture and what interventions would be required to get Evergreen on solid ground. I needed to see how revenue was flowing in and out of the business and examine key financial indicators. Standard financial reporting processes were not in place, so data needed to be collected from various sources and pulled together. This in itself turned out to be quite a challenge.

When I asked Dr. Bradford what financial reports she looked at each month, she expressed frustration. The practice management system generated many reports, but no one was looking at them or providing Dr. Bradford with sound financial information about the practice.

Cheryl Alexander, the practice administrator, was in charge of finances, but told Dr. Bradford she didn't have time to look at the monthly reports, yet alone analyze them. Cheryl simply knew that the amount of money collected each month was not enough to cover Evergreen's expenses. She cared deeply about the practice and was losing sleep over the state of financial affairs.

Annual financial statistics on OB-GYN practices compiled by the National Society of Certified Healthcare Business Consultants (NSCHBC) and Medical Group Management Association (MGMA) were used to conduct a comparative financial analysis of Evergreen Women's Center.

The Revenue Cycle

First I needed to look at the charges, receipts, adjustments and accounts receivable (A/R) for the practice to find out if Evergreen was collecting what should be expected, based on other OB-GYN group practices across

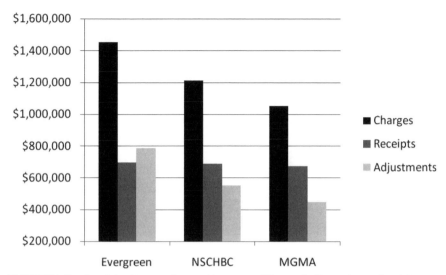

FIGURE 1. Productivity Comparisons. Evergreen Women's Center's productivity performance comparison, per full-time equivalent MD. MGMA = Medical Group Management Association; NSCHBC = National Society of Certified Healthcare Business Consultants.

the nation. These comparisons would help determine if revenue-recovery strategies could be implemented to pump up cash flow.

The first red flag was obvious: this practice's charges and adjustments were higher than the average for its peers, but its receipts were dismal (Figure 1). The practice was collecting only 48% of its charges, as opposed to collection rates of 56.8% reported by NSCHBC and 63.8% reported by MGMA. If Evergreen's collection rate was 63.8%, it would have earned nearly $230,000 (per physician) in additional income during the previous year. This would have provided considerable relief to the present financial situation.

Evergreen Women's Center's adjustments (contractual allowances) were 54% of charges compared with an average of 45.6% reported by NSCHBC and 42.6% reported by MGMA. This is usually an indicator of inappropriate adjustments, poor-performing contracts or an unusually high fee schedule (charge master).

I soon discovered that Evergreen's billing department was struggling. The data entry, billing and collection staff members were inundated because of the rapid growth. Systems were not in place to handle the growth and volume. Work was coming to them faster than they could handle it.

Claims submission was delayed by as much as 30 days due to the high volume, and, according to a frustrated staff, there was no time to follow up on claims. To top it off, many claims were being rejected because the patient demographics were incomplete or inaccurate. These issues contributed to above-average A/R as exhibited in Table 1, more than 50% above the average OB-GYN practice. Evergreen's money was on the books instead of in the bank.

TABLE 1. Accounts Receivable Details for Evergreen vs. Industry Averages

Description	Evergreen	NSCHBC	MGMA
Total $ of A/R	191,894	116,383	108,378
A/R % aged >90 Days	34	Unknown	18.06
Days in A/R	63	48	39.41

A/R = accounts receivable; MGMA = Medical Group Management Association; NSCHBC = National Society of Certified Healthcare Business Consultants.

On the back end, when payments came in there was a rush to get the money deposited. Payments were not scrutinized before they were posted, and not enough time was dedicated to analyzing claims to be sure they were adjudicated properly before adjustments were posted. There were instances when the billing staff was inadvertently adjusting-off balances inappropriately, resulting in lost revenue to the practice. This cost Evergreen plenty!

Expense Control

A review of the top expenses for OB-GYN practices reveals that four expense categories account for the majority of expense, as shown in Table 2. Staffing

TABLE 2. Evergreen's Highest Expenses vs. Industry Average (% of gross income)

Description	Evergreen	NSCHBC	MGMA
Staffing	39	24	30
Staff benefits	7	3.8	6.3
Rent	9	5.8	6.6
Malpractice insurance	6	6.4	5.3
Combined total	61	40	48.2
Other operating expense	17	20.8	11.5
Total practice operating expense	**78**	**60.8**	**59.7**

MGMA = Medical Group Management Association; NSCHBC = National Society of Certified Healthcare Business Consultants.

expense and staff benefits alone account for 46% of Evergreen's overhead compared with a 27.8% average reported by NSCHBC and 36.3% reported by MGMA. Staffing costs and efficiency required Evergreen's immediate attention. Compared with industry averages, rent was higher for Evergreen as well, suggesting it would be important to be more productive to increase income and utilize space to generate additional revenue where appropriate.

Total operating expenses averaged slightly more than 60% of receipts as reported by NSCHBC and close to 60% reported by MGMA. Unfortunately, Evergreen Women's Center's expenses were far higher—an alarming 78% of gross income. This excessive overhead expense left Evergreen with only 22% of its gross income to pay the physicians and pay down the debt. It wasn't enough! Expenses were killing this practice.

THE INFRASTRUCTURE

The administrative review revealed an administrative vacuum, a large contributor to Evergreen's problems. Dr. Bradford was a respected leader and was, without question, the driving force behind the practice's growth and community presence. However, the infrastructure was weak. Throughout the hierarchy, there were no clear expectations or accountability. There was little delineation of duties and responsibilities, beginning with the administrator all the way down to the file clerk.

Too much was being expected of Cheryl, the administrator. Her role needed to be clearly defined and designed to utilize her talents. She had a strong financial background and was devoted to the practice. Her analytical skills made her a fine candidate to handle the practice finances but she needed direction and structure.

Cheryl preferred working with finances and was frustrated by the other responsibilities that seemed to sabotage her ability to focus on the financial picture. It was easy to see why Cheryl was unable to dedicate time to performing financial analysis. She was bombarded with day-to-day problems that she didn't have the time to deal with, and her workload was unmanageable. She was trying to handle the finances and practice administration while being pulled into crisis situations. In addition, the physicians would continually call upon her to handle minor projects. With proper planning, it was reasonable to assume that many of these projects could be delegated to other staff members.

TABLE 3. OB-GYN Group Practice Staffing Benchmark Comparatives

Organization	Staff (per FTE physician)
Evergreen	6.1
NSCHBC	4.29
MGMA	4.57

FTE = full-time equivalents; MGMA= Medical Group Management Association; NSCHBC = National Society of Certified Healthcare Business Consultants.

Staffing

Staff growth was out of control and resulted in staffing levels far above the norm (Table 3) with poor definition of roles. If one department said it needed help and couldn't manage the workload, another staffer was recruited. This occurred without analyzing efficiency or work processes that would define the actual need. In other words, staff was increased based on perceived needs rather than determining actual needs. Not only was this a financial concern, it represented a loss of control and was a source of frustration throughout the organization.

There were no written job descriptions. Without a clear delineation of duties, there was no way to know what was expected of staff members. In addition, work measurement tools were not in place, making it difficult (if not impossible) for employees to know if they were doing a good job. This also compromised the ability to measure productivity at every level. The best performers were not being recognized, and there were no consequences for under performance.

How Decisions Were Made

Planning was inadequate, resulting in poor decision making. The practice was reacting to circumstances rather than acting on information. It seemed Dr. Bradford was always called upon to intervene when problems erupted that required a management decision. The practice resorted to continual "crisis management." This was both inefficient and costly to the practice.

The organizational chart was linear, drawing too few people into authoritative, decision-making positions. There were only three levels on the organizational chart:

- Physician/owner (Dr. Bradford);
- Administrator (Cheryl Alexander); and

- Everyone else.

This linear approach to the organization was choking Dr. Bradford and Cheryl. It contributed to the loss of control, poor decision making and inadequate management resources. Cheryl did not meet regularly with Dr. Bradford to discuss emerging issues and concerns. At the same time, Dr. Bradford did not meet with the other physicians or include them in any of management's decisions.

There were no staff meetings to keep staff connected, provide support among staff members and different departments or to communicate information about the practice. Communication was often disseminated through informal channels, such as when only one staff member was told about a change that impacted an entire department. Naturally this staff member would be left to his or her own discretion to relay information to other employees. This approach to communication was wide open to subjective interpretation and delivered throughout the organization with inconsistency. Often sensitive information told to one person in confidence ended up in the rumor mill, causing considerable distress and confusion.

THE FINAL DIAGNOSIS

Although Evergreen's problems seemed overwhelming, once the situation was thoroughly explored six major contributors to the practice's state of affairs were identified. Addressing these factors was essential to getting the practice back on course.

1. No clear direction;
2. Lack of planning;
3. Inadequate infrastructure;
4. Poor use of resources;
5. Lack of financial management; and
6. Improper decision making.

NO PAIN, NO GAIN

Immediate interventions were required, and tough decisions needed to be made to help this practice survive. This required an aggressive survival plan: pumping up the revenue and cutting expenses to the core. It included a reduction in staff and some temporary pay cuts. Dr. Bradford's commitment to the practice and loyalty to staff and patients made it difficult for her to accept this reality, but it was time to put emotions aside.

Efforts focused on stopping the flow of red ink, strengthening the administrative arm of the practice and developing effective methods to monitor critical financial data. This was a challenge that required both a swift, decisive plan and the support of management and staff. Dr. Bradford was ready to listen to her advisors and do what was necessary to save the practice.

TURNAROUND STRATEGIES

The key components for a successful turnaround included:
- Responding to critical data;
- Defining expectations;
- Eliminating waste and duplication;
- Implementing and adhering to a budget;
- Planning effectively and improving decision making;
- Developing a skilled leadership team; and
- Improving communication throughout the organization.

Interim Leadership Team

It was critical to recruit an administrator with the leadership, organizational and business talents essential to oversee the practice's operations and business performance. From past experience, I knew this could easily take three to four months. In the meantime, Dr. Bradford agreed to have my consulting team provide interim leadership services. The consulting team was charged with the reorganization, leading the financial turnaround and implementing sound financial strategies.

Cheryl was reassigned to the position of staff accountant, which freed her to provide the consultants with constant status reports on practice finances. She was relieved to have someone else assume responsibility for handling the practice's administrative burdens and decision making during this critical transition.

The success of the turnaround was dependent on selecting a project coordinator to work closely with the consultants to carry out staff assignments and be our communication link. Angela Lopez, the lead biller, was a logical choice. She had previous management experience, possessed organizational and leadership skills and was respected by the staff. She was totally committed to Evergreen and was invaluable as the point person.

THE ACTION PLAN

The first response to critical data was placing an immediate freeze on hiring and capital spending, followed by an analysis of staff duties and performance to increase output. A financial-recovery plan was developed to maximize resources and expedite billing and collection activities.

The obvious approach to getting this practice on a sound financial footing was dependent on five basic objectives:

1. Maximize physician and staff productivity;
2. Improve charge capture;
3. Optimize revenue recovery;
4. Reduce expenses; and
5. Control capital outlay.

Action grids were prepared outlining responsibilities of the consultant team and the staff accountant (Figures 2 and 3). These action grids were reviewed with Dr. Bradford, the other physicians, Cheryl and Angela. It was important for each of these people to understand the goals and the commitment necessary to move the practice through difficult times. Without their support, it would be a hard road to recovery.

In the end, everyone wanted the same things: direction, structure, stability and financial viability. The staff and physicians understood this would not be easy to achieve and would require their support. Through mutual respect, flexibility and building a solid foundation, progress continued at a reasonable pace and confidence in the practice was eventually restored.

Before the action plan was implemented, two meetings were scheduled to discuss the dire state of affairs, communicate the need for immediate recovery actions and solicit support. This required careful and deliberate planning to ensure the physicians and staff would have hope for the future of the practice and commit to the changes required to achieve viability for a practice that appeared to have a dynamic future—if only it could get its finances under control.

These meetings set the record straight and truncated the distorted grapevine approach to communication that previously relayed inaccurate information, resulting in fear and diminished confidence in management's ability to solve major problems. It was time to lay the cards on the table and tell everyone about the practice's financial situation and let them know how it would be resolved. This was particularly difficult for Dr. Bradford,

CONSULTANT TEAM / INTERIM ADMINISTRATOR		
Action	**Deadline**	**Purpose**
Select project coordinator	Immediate	Provide coordination and support of required actions
Recruit and hire new administrator	60 days	Improve leadership and organizational function
Assign staff members to complete job description questionnaire for creating new job descriptions	3 days	Understand current workflow
Collect workload data	10 days	Evaluate staffing needs to improve efficiency
Establish and enforce collection criteria	7 days	Improve cash flow
Assign billing supervisor and establish collection criteria/goals	Immediate	Empower and mentor billing staff
Establish charge reporting and claims submission time limits	7 days	Tighten revenue cycle, improve cash flow
Implement improved coding application and charge reporting	10 days	Improve financial performance
Conduct payer analysis and renegotiate with or terminate poor-performing contracts where contract terms permit	90 days	Improve financial performance
Develop job descriptions and performance standards	7 days	Improve accountability
Establish staff productivity measures	10 days	Improve productivity
Reassign and/or terminate unnecessary positions	10 days	Improve operational efficiency
Establish temporary pay rate adjustments for physicians and staff	15 days	Reduce monthly expenses
Reduce long-term staffing costs to national benchmark levels	30 days	Reduce operating costs
Develop monthly physician productivity goals	30 days	Increase revenue
Establish regular business management and staff meetings	30 days	Improve communication, cooperation and decision making
Sublet space for new office	60 days	Reduce overhead

FIGURE 2. Action grid for the consultant team.

STAFF ACCOUNTANT		
Action	**Deadline**	**Purpose**
Prepare weekly cash flow report	Every Monday	Improve communication of financial position, monitor trends and allow for sound financial planning
Prepare weekly aged receivable report with graphic presentation	Every Monday	Improve communication of financial position, monitor trends and allow for sound financial planning
Prepare monthly graphs • Productivity reports by MD/provider • New and established patient visits by provider • Procedures and deliveries • Referral sources • Accounts receivable management • Payer mix/performance	7th of each month	Improve communication of financial position, monitor trends and allow for sound financial planning
Prepare analytical report on top 10 payers mix and financial performance	30 days	Improve communication of financial position, monitor trends and allow for sound financial planning
Collaborate with interim administrator on financial planning	Once a week	Improve communication of financial position, monitor trends and allow for sound financial planning
Reduce operating expenses and stop capital spending	Immediately	Apply sound financial principles
Negotiate vendor payment terms	Immediately	Reduce financial pressures
Explore options/cost reduction for malpractice, group health and workers' compensation insurance	Immediately	Reduce operating expense
Conduct supply-vendor cost analysis, including group purchasing	15 days	Reduce supply costs
Renegotiate loan payments on capital debt	Immediately	Reduce monthly financial outlay
Prepare practice budget	60 days	Improve financial management

FIGURE 3. Action grid for the staff accountant.

as she was not accustomed to sharing information or involving staff in the practice's business affairs. It required several management meetings to agree on what information needed to be shared with the employees—in fairness to them and to obtain their support. We wanted the staff to know the situation was serious, but that a recovery plan was in place. The consultant team knew there was hope for the future, and this was the picture we intended to paint.

The first meeting was with the physicians. Once they understood the gravity of the practice's finances, they agreed to a request to reduce their salaries by 10% for six months, with a payback of six equal payments beginning in 24 months. It was further explained that the goal was to have the practice on sound financial footing within 12 to 18 months, so partnership agreements could be pursued. The physicians were promised that they would receive monthly reports to keep them abreast of the practice's financial performance.

The second meeting included the entire staff. In this meeting, we explained the practice's position and the necessity to reassign some positions and reduce staffing costs. We asked for people to consider the option of reducing their work hours or volunteering to be furloughed. Immediately following this meeting, each staff member met individually with Dr. Bradford and one of the consultants to discuss his or her own situation and options. We explained that each position would be reevaluated and structured so that productivity could be measured and we could capitalize on the individual strengths of staff members.

This entire process was difficult and emotional for Dr. Bradford but was essential to move the practice out of the red. Several employees resigned; but for the most part, staff members wanted to support Evergreen Women's Center and were willing to reduce their hours, roll up their sleeves and become part of the solution. This was encouraging.

THE RESULTS

During the three months it took to obtain a top-notch administrator, efforts focused on communication, building a strong infrastructure, accountability and improving finances.

Once the new administrator was in place, progress followed rapidly. Within 12 months, the financial-recovery plan was complete, and the practice was able to begin repayment to the physicians for the initial six-month cut back in pay.

During the implementation of the turnaround, some difficult business decisions were made. These decisions were essential to getting Evergreen Women's Center on solid ground and accomplishing the stated objectives:

- Improved leadership and communication;
- Monthly monitoring of critical financial data;
- Increased collections;
- Debt reduction;
- Improved cash flow;
- Controlled growth;
- Increased physician and staff productivity; and
- Higher physician and staff satisfaction.

The entire recovery process was valuable in teaching all the physicians some sound business principles for managing the practice and monitoring financial performance. Evergreen Women's Center achieved group viability, improved operating performance and financial stability.

THE NEXT STEP

The old saying "failure to plan is planning to fail" was a reality Evergreen Women's Center didn't want to experience again. Fifteen months after the practice reorganization began, the physicians and management team participated in a strategic planning session. Together, they clarified future goals for the practice and determined the financial resources and strategies required to achieve the stated goals. This was accomplished through market research, demographic analysis and gaining an understanding of Evergreen's market strengths and weaknesses.

The strategic planning process included an examination of potential opportunities within the community to expand the practice and the services Evergreen had to offer. At the same time, it was important to explore potential concerns including what perceived or existing competitors and market conditions might pose a threat to Evergreen's ability to draw on its strengths. Examining these issues was critical to developing a realistic strategic plan. At last, Evergreen Women's Center understood the importance of strategic planning to prepare for the future and guide its actions. The physicians and the administrator of Evergreen Women's Group closely examined their options before making decisions that would affect their future. In the end, the strategic plan was designed to serve as Evergreen Women's Center's blueprint for the future.

Within 18 months of Dr. Bradford's first call to my office, she was able to offer the other physicians partnership into a practice with a stable future. Evergreen Women's Center now takes a methodical, carefully crafted approach to growth. Their future is more predictable and far more secure.

Evergreen Women's Center is a fine-tuned practice that now stands out from the crowd. Without question, its solid infrastructure, approach to decision making and cautious regard for managing finances makes it a top-performing practice.

THE SECRETS

1. Uncontrolled growth can result in a loss of control and financial hardship.
2. Strategic planning puts you in charge of your future.
3. A demand for your services does not guarantee your success.
4. Establish reporting methods that help identify red flags in practice performance.
5. Practice finances must be monitored and "managed" before a crisis emerges.
6. Develop a solid infrastructure that supports future growth.
7. Clarify job responsibilities to improve efficiency.
8. Productivity measures improve output.
9. Adding staff is not always the solution to improving output.
10. Prompt action is required to overcome financial problems.
11. Financially plan and budget for practice growth.

FORM ADDED TO YOUR TOOLBOX:

☞ *Sample Organizational Chart: Group OB-GYN Practice*

CHAPTER 12

Reshaping the Practice— A New Genre

W ith not enough money and too many demands upon their time, many physicians with traditional medical practices are looking at ways to improve their practice. They want to serve their patients better, but often struggle with the dynamics of running a medical practice.

There is so much pressure and influence from outside the practice—everything from increasingly demanding patients to lower reimbursement rates and a government that scrutinizes doctors and changes the rules. This constant barrage affects the medical practice and choices physicians make.

The physician's goal is to unload these worries and get back to enjoying his or her patients. In this quest, they look for ways to reshape the practice and redirect its focus. Whatever opportunity a physician pursues, whether it's creating a "concierge" type practice, moving toward sports medicine or adding more diverse services, the success of a new genre depends on taking the right approach.

Don't impulsively change your practice. Just because Dr. Marcus down the street starts doing bone density studies or adds a treadmill doesn't mean it's right for your practice to follow suit. Looking for new sources of revenue or ways to improve the practice's services is reasonable, but expanding your services requires careful and deliberate planning.

WHAT DO YOU WANT TO DO?

If you are looking for ways to revamp the practice by attracting different patients, changing the services you provide or adopting a new practice philosophy, you had better look within before you begin. Your commitment is essential. What can you commit to and feel passionate about? In what areas do you excel? In this early assessment stage, concentrate on being honest with yourself and avoiding undue outside influences such as what you think makes financial sense. Focus on your talent and passion. Accurate self-examination is critical to making a successful major transition in what you do and how you do it. An expert in strategic planning can help you avoid making mistakes that might have serious consequences.

DOING IT RIGHT

Start with a commitment to an exploratory process that includes everything from soul-searching and analyzing your strengths to examining what opportunities are available and what makes sense, based on market needs, your talents and what you really want. But don't expect a yellow-brick road that will lead you to your ultimate destination—it's not that simple! You must match the practice's desire and skill sets with existing opportunities. There are a few critical questions you must answer:

1. Is there a demand for the service?
2. Is someone else already providing the service?
3. Who is my competition?
4. Can I do it better than the competition?
5. How will I attract patients?
6. How long will it take to meet my market potential?

Once you decide to move forward, you'll need a solid plan for integrating and marketing the service—whether it's just to your own patients or to a broader market.

If the genre you plan to offer involves a financial commitment, you'll want to conduct a feasibility study to understand the market, analyze your return on investment and project your break-even point. This examination considers your current position in the marketplace and other factors, such as your image in the community, patient attitudes and impact upon staff and operations.

MAKING IT HAPPEN

If you want something in the practice to change, you—the physician and manager—must lead. As the catalyst, your commitment will make the difference. Some physicians come up with their own ideas about something new they can offer their patients. Others simply want to get on board with the latest trend—doing stress testing, DEXA scans, weight management, you name it! These efforts are destined to fail without a strong commitment. Here are examples of some of your peers that have successfully made major changes within their practices and reaped the rewards of their commitment.

THE BOUTIQUE PRACTICE

I met with Paul Block, M.D., a previous client of mine in Thousand Oaks, California, one year after he signed on with MDVIP to establish a concierge practice. I asked him why he made such a dramatic shift in his practice model. He told me, "It's all about time! I wanted more time with my patients. It's been a wise decision. I love it and so do they!"

Dr. Block was one of three physicians in a nearly 30-year-old group internal medicine/pulmonary practice. He watched overhead climb and reimbursement decline for more than 10 years. To survive financially, Dr. Block, like physicians across the country, went into survival mode—volume! This meant seeing more patients. He was dissatisfied with this style of medicine and yearned for the "good old days" when physicians knew their patients, patients were loyal and visits were unhurried. He fondly recalled the days when hospital executives and physicians worked without conflicting objectives. By 2004, this just wasn't a reality.

The Reality Check

The demands of patient care have changed dramatically. Thirty years ago, a primary care physician managed fewer than 1,000 patients; now each manages more than 2,500. Additionally, insurance companies are the primary source for adding new patients to the practice. Physicians are being rushed, and patients are less satisfied.

Self-Examination

For over one year, Dr. Block considered his practice and his motivations and wondered what he could do to get back to the patient care model he enjoyed so much in the 1970s. He had heard about boutique medicine—the concierge-type practice that focuses on specialized care, serving fewer patients and giving each one more time. This concept seemed too good to be true: having enough time with patients to know them as individuals, carefully probe their history and provide a detailed exam without feeling rushed. It sounded like a page from history, but his curiosity and desire to provide better service for his patients drove him to further explore the "boutique" practice model.

Checking It Out

Dr. Block met representatives from MDVIP, a corporation that specializes in helping physicians develop a boutique practice. He learned about its philosophy and methods for converting an established practice to a practice with personalized healthcare. The success of such a practice requires scaling down the practice, reducing the patient volume to as little as 25% of a typical primary care doctor. This allows the physician to dedicate far more time to each patient. Initial consultations are 90 minutes, and a half-hour is dedicated to acute and follow-up visits. In order to make this system work, patients need to commit to paying for the doctor's time. Since the MDVIP physician dedicates his practice to a smaller number of patients, fewer than 600, he is more accessible to the patient and can dedicate more time to each of them.

With the MDVIP physician, each patient is charged an annual fee of $1,800 that includes:

- **Preventive care physical exam:** The physical exam is extensive and much more involved than the traditional "comprehensive exam." In Dr. Block's practice, it includes a nutritional evaluation, an activity assessment to examine activities of daily living, a sleep questionnaire, a mini-mental status and depression assessment and a complete examination and assessment. During this visit, Dr. Block dedicates not only the time he needs to conduct the examination, but as much time as the patient needs to get his or her questions answered and be reassured.
- **Comprehensive wellness and lifestyle planning:** It's highly unlikely that physicians in traditional medicine have time to address this in the limited time spent with a patient visit.
- **Personal health record CD-ROM.**

It took Dr. Block more than a year to recognize that this was the niche he was looking for—a way to practice medicine the way it was done in the '70s.

The Transition

Dr. Block decided to move forward. MDVIP's corporate services staff members helped convert the practice by supplying materials and support. They briefed him on what to expect and were available for handholding.

MDVIP sponsored seminars for his patients during the transition and also held a workshop for staff on patient relations. Dr. Block was directed to set up this new practice model and make it truly patient-focused. MDVIP provides on-going support once the practice comes on board. It provides a newsletter and tracks patient outcomes by monitoring emergency room visits and hospitalization.

Reflecting on the Change

"When you are taking care of 2,500 patients, you don't have time to get to know each of them, and it's frustrating. You feel like a hamster in a cage, going round and round. Concierge (boutique) medicine is about time—taking time to give each patient more care and build relationships with your patients— really getting to know each one of them and being there for them whenever they need you," Dr. Block told me when we met. "I'm on call 24/7, and it's fine with me—it's what I want to do to provide the best quality care for my patients." He is also available by email and keeps in close contact with his patients. It seems the patients love this and are willing to pay for it, and according to Dr. Block, it's not the wealthiest patients that sign on.

It has now been a year since Dr. Block became an MDVIP physician. I asked him if he has any regrets. He reflected for a few minutes, looked up and said, "No, this really works for me and for my patients." He is calm, and he is happy. His passion for medicine has been revived.

SHIFTING TO COSMETICS

Plastic reconstructive surgeons are dedicated physicians. Their reconstructive talents are amazing. They transform the lives of people forever by changing the way patients look and feel about themselves. Take the child born with a birth defect that distorts half of his face. The skilled plastic surgeon corrects this so the child looks and feels normal. What about the burn victim who needs multiple plastic surgeries to reconstruct her body? The results are incredible. These are awesome responsibilities. But with the advent of managed care, there's another side to this coin that makes life for the reconstructive surgeon difficult.

The Changing Economics

Medicine is a business, and the insurance companies have hit plastic reconstructive surgeons with this reality. They have ratcheted down the fees they pay for delicate reconstructive surgery and continually scrutinize the need for such services. This often puts the surgeon in the position of having to justify the necessity for surgery, involving excessive time and reams of paperwork for the physician's staff. With this squeeze put on dedicated plastic reconstructive surgeons, they begin to look at ways to make the practice less vulnerable. Marshall Grainger, M.D., a prominent plastic surgeon, was no exception.

About the Practice

Dr. Grainger called my office. He had a very busy reconstructive surgery practice in the northwest and particularly enjoyed working with children. He volunteered each year to spend time doing reconstructive surgery in under-developed countries and had earned quite an international reputation. Typically, 75% of his patients required reconstructive surgery, and the remainder had elective cosmetic procedures and paid out-of-pocket. The cosmetic cases were enjoyable, but his first love was reconstructive surgery. Unfortunately, his reconstructive practice was feeling the pinch of managed care—both on staffing needs and financially.

In the previous three years, Dr. Grainger doubled the number of staff members in his insurance department. Meanwhile, reimbursement for reconstructive surgery continued to drop. After 20 years of practice, Dr. Grainger knew he needed to make a shift. He could not do enough reconstructive procedures to make up for lower reimbursement, increased overhead costs and his volunteer work.

Moving In a New Direction

It was time to increase the ratio of cosmetic surgery procedures. For the previous six months, Dr. Grainger had presented several community lectures on cosmetic surgery in an effort to attract more patients. Still, there was little change in the practice mix. I was called in to suggest ways to increase the number of elective procedures.

I spent a day with the practice, interviewing the entire staff and watching as they worked. I examined appointment schedules for past months and the next month. I talked to the manager and the receptionist/scheduler about Dr. Grainger's intent to shift to more cosmetic procedures. Dr. Grainger had indeed told staff members (six months prior) that he wanted to perform more cosmetic procedures and asked Sarah, the receptionist, to be sure and accommodate any patient calling for a cosmetic appointment, but that's as far as it went. No goals were set, and there was little preparation or thought given to how this practice could actually change its patient base.

Digging Deeper

I looked at the statistics on the number of cosmetic versus reconstructive consults that were performed in the office the previous quarter. This revealed a 74/26 ratio—74% were reconstructive patients. When I compared this to the same quarter the prior year, it showed only a slight variation.

The receptionist was probed on her scheduling techniques. This revealed that reconstructive and cosmetic consultations were handled in the same way: The patient would be offered the next available appointment—usually a two- or three-week wait. This wait was longer than desirable for a cosmetic surgery practice. It's important with elective services to expedite getting patients into the office—while they are highly motivated.

The past appointment schedule also showed that 20% of patients scheduled for new cosmetic consultations were not showing up for their appointments. In addition to these no-shows, there were patients that called for an appointment but didn't schedule because the next available appointment was two or three weeks away.

What was Dr. Grainger's staff doing to make this practice cosmetic-patient friendly? Very little! There were six major internal factors that contributed to the lack of growth in cosmetic procedures:

1. The practice did not define specific cosmetic patient goals and time frames to accomplish them.
2. There was no template that reserved a specific number of appointment slots for new cosmetic patients.
3. There were no grouped time slots specifically for cosmetic patients. This resulted in these patients being sandwiched between reconstructive patient appointments—not a good mix, because of the very different needs and attitudes of these two types of patients. Also, dealing with the variables in these patient types requires a different mindset for staff. For example, with patients that need reconstructive surgery, staff must focus on insurance coverage issues and informing patients of the necessary wait to obtain authorization for surgery. With cosmetic patients, the focus is on obtaining a commitment and discussing the costs and payment for services.

4. There was no post-consult summary to discuss finances, answer questions and schedule the cosmetic surgery.
5. No protocol was in place to record inquiries about cosmetic procedures, eliminating the ability to monitor staff's rate of converting inquiries to patients.
6. There were no tracking tools in place to follow the cosmetic patients.

The physician and staff were too close to the situation to realize they were placing cosmetic patients in a difficult position. Cosmetic patients may be uncomfortable and feel superficial and vain when they wait in the reception room with disfigured patients whose surgical needs are far greater. Cosmetic services are elective, and their visit experience must be positive from the time they first call the office until their consult appointment is complete.

Moving In the Right Direction

To improve Dr. Grainger's cosmetic procedure ratio, we began by establishing sensible growth targets. We used the previous quarter's statistical ratio to develop realistic quarterly goals for shifting the numbers (Table 1).

TABLE 1. Goals for Increasing Cosmetic Consultations

Time Period	Cosmetic (% of consults)	Reconstructive (% of consults)
Prior 4th quarter (baseline)	26	74
1st quarter	30	70
2nd quarter	40	60
3rd quarter	50	50
4th quarter	60	40

In order to achieve the established goals, a scheduling template was developed. The template reserved slots specifically for cosmetic patients, and the number reserved was in line with the ratio of cosmetic patients required to meet the quarterly goals. These scheduling slots were concurrent so that specific mornings and afternoons were dedicated to cosmetic patients. This did not interfere with the services provided for reconstructive patients and did not place the cosmetic patient in an uncomfortable position.

Beyond this, with the cosmetic consultations being seen in specific time blocks, the staff members were able to give each patient the attention required. Each cosmetic patient was given a full half hour with the physician, followed by a half hour for computer imaging and consultation with the coordinator of cosmetic services.

The coordinator of cosmetic services managed the cosmetic program as well. When a patient hesitated to schedule a consultation with the scheduler, the call was transferred to the coordinator to increase the conversion rate. She also tracked all inquiries, appointments and procedures through the use of a database enabling patients to receive timely office mailings, including information about upcoming seminars and special events.

The actual numbers were monitored to see if further adjustments were needed down the road, but the practice remained on target and exceeded its goals (Figure 1).

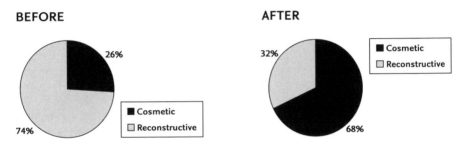

BEFORE   **AFTER**

FIGURE 1. Ratio of cosmetic and reconstructive procedures before and after the new measures were adopted.

A World of Difference

Within a year, the conversion rate from inquiry to appointment for cosmetic patients jumped 30%. Beyond this, 75% of these patients scheduled cosmetic surgery. The practice also added a skin center program that sells top-of-the-line skin care products and conducts skin care workshops.

Dr. Grainger has benefited from some wonderful publicity for his work with cosmetic patients, creating additional demand for his services. Since Dr. Grainger has every intention of dedicating at least 25% of his time to reconstructive patients, he has hired a new associate. With a well-trained, dedicated staff, the patients are accepting the new associate and she is building a solid patient base. Dr. Grainger has created the perfect balance to expand the cosmetic genre while continuing the reconstructive and volunteer work that is so important to him.

GOING BARIATRICS

Long before celebrities Al Roker and Carnie Wilson ever thought about gastric bypass surgery, I received a call from Robert Harris, M.D., a young general surgeon that wanted to make this the focus of his practice. Dr. Harris had performed bariatric surgery for several years and was the only surgeon in town doing this procedure. He observed his patients' response closely and was impressed with the way the resulting weight loss changed the health, attitude and quality of life for them. He was committed to continue this work and enthused about making it a major part of his practice.

Dr. Harris hired an advertising specialist and created a slick four-color brochure and an advertising campaign that included community outreach. By the time he contacted me, several months had passed, and he was disappointed with the results. He was performing only three to five gastric bypass surgeries a month, a marginal increase over his pre-marketing days. Something seemed wrong, but he wasn't sure what it was.

The Practice

Dr. Harris ran a typical general surgery practice with three staffers in a 1,400 square foot office. His manager, Marie, ran the front desk and handled all of the phone calls, scheduling, billing and reception duties. The nurse, Anna, had worked with Dr. Harris for the past 12 years and was immersed in the practice. The patients knew and loved her. The third staff person was Chandra, a part-time medical assistant that worked both the front and back office. She cleaned the exam rooms, autoclaved instruments, answered phones and did the filing.

Everyone had a job to do and seemed to manage it with precision. The problem was, they had no idea how to help Dr. Harris build a bariatric practice. They watched the advertising agency come in and out of the office, heard talk about a direct mail campaign, saw bundles of the slick brochure and listened to Dr. Harris talk about doing more gastric bypass surgeries, but they never related this to their jobs or anything concrete. This meant patients that called about gastric bypass were treated like every other patient—there was little procedural difference, other than scheduling their psychological evaluation and pre-surgical history and physical.

Strengthening His Position

My first recommendation to Dr. Harris was to obtain a toll-free phone number specifically for bypass surgery inquiries. This dedicated line, along with bypass surgery inquiries that came into the regular phone line, needed to be fielded by someone in the office whose main focus was gastric bypass patients—answering their questions, scheduling their appointments, participating in their work-up and coordinating their care. It also required providing on-going support for these sometimes-apprehensive patients.

Since Anna, the nurse, had no interest in this type of position and no time to spare, I suggested hiring a nurse educator and training her on all aspects of gastric bypass. The nurse educator would also be responsible for tracking the calls, consultations and number of consultations that resulted in surgical procedures. She would also be the liaison with the advertising agency, coordinating activities and following through on recommendations.

The Nurse Educator

Finding someone to fill the role of nurse educator was not difficult. As in most cases, there were many nurses seeking to move beyond the traditional role of hospital nurse. Twenty-five nurses applied for the position, and we found just the right candidate. Diana was a confident, conscientious, out-going nurse with experience in the operating room and on the surgical floor of the community hospital. She exuded enthusiasm and confidence, and she was an independent worker. To top it off, she had great organizational skills.

With Diana's assistance, I developed protocols on how to handle everything from the first phone call to the patient's one-year follow-up exam and everything in between. Diana went to surgery with Dr. Harris and learned as much as she could about the procedure. She talked with previous patients and met with each of them when they came in for follow-up. She found out what their needs were and learned all about theirs fears. Within six months, Diana developed a support group that was a major hit. Past patients gave testimonials, and people considering surgery came in to gather information and learn more about the procedure—what to expect and how it affected patients. When people called the office to talk about gastric bypass, Diana would give them her full attention and whatever time they needed to get their questions answered.

Contact information for both patients and those who inquired about the procedure were placed in a database. These people received a newsletter and were invited to attend the support group meetings. Within three years, Dr. Harris was known throughout the county for his work in bariatrics and was featured in area newspapers. Some patients were coming from 500 miles away to seek his services.

Within five years, Dr. Harris' practice was limited to bariatric patients. He has proctored other physicians and has gained a national reputation. Diana is still with him, and he contributes his success to her involvement. Dr. Harris is on the cutting edge of change in bariatric procedures and has an incredibly dynamic practice.

OTHER OPPORTUNITIES

There are a multitude of ways physicians can reshape their practices to meet new demands and a changing healthcare economy. Holistic practices, once thought to be on the edge, are now becoming mainstream. Patients in all parts of the country are seeking physicians that offer complementary and alternative medicine (CAM) services. A number of physicians find that some of these services blend well with their traditional practice. These CAM services not only provide an additional revenue stream to the practice, but they also provide increased convenience for patients.

Travel medicine can be a great practice builder for the primary care physician. There are also weight reduction programs and programs that focus on health and fitness, whether it is sports medicine for the orthopaedic surgeon or nutrition or exercise programs for a variety of specialists. Some OB-GYN practices are expanding their services by looking at the total woman and developing wellness and weight management programs.

A forward-thinking OB-GYN practice looking for an additional revenue stream might even consider collaborating with a local gym to offer memberships to patients of the practice. Such a business venture could be expanded to sell products, such as exercise videos, work-out clothing and maternity wear with the practice logo. Pediatricians could easily collaborate with OB-GYN practices in developing "Mommy and Me" and "Preparing for Motherhood" programs.

There are a multitude of ways physicians can expand their practices and better serve both their patients and the community. The opportunities are limited only by the imagination. Of course, physicians must be careful to engage in activities that support their mission and maintain the professional dignity of the practice.

IN THE END

You can change the direction or focus of the practice—whether you want to add or eliminate certain services, appeal to a different consumer or size up or down. If you are committed, dedicate time and resources to explore your options and develop a solid strategic plan, you can create a new genre that defines your future. You have choices: It's your practice, your business.

THE SECRETS

1. You have choices in reshaping your practice.
2. Respond to the marketplace.
3. Don't feel compelled to mimic your competition or follow the latest fad.
4. Self-examination is vital to successfully changing the services you offer.
5. Plan carefully, and dedicate time and resources to shifting your practice's services.
6. The success of a new genre is rooted in your commitment.

FORM ADDED TO YOUR TOOLBOX:

⤺ *Guidelines for Strategic Planning*

CHAPTER 13

Smart-Sourcing for the Savvy Practice

O utsourcing has become a major contributor to reducing costs and providing relief for big business, but it can also be a very smart move for medical practices. With rising costs and tight controls on reimbursement and

the need for a higher level of business acumen to run a medical office, physicians are finding it necessary to dig deeper into expenses and find ways to reduce costs while tapping into an equal or higher level of expertise to get things accomplished for the practice.

I suggest that practices turn to "smart-sourcing"—a balance of outsourcing, insourcing and leveraging available talent. I call it "smart-sourcing" because when it is done right, it is a smart thing to do. The first step is recognizing you may need resources outside the practice to meet your business needs. Then it's a matter of seeking ways to manage costs, increase efficiency and keep the practice growing without compromising quality. The keys to making a smart choice are clarifying your motivation and the gains you hope to achieve; selecting the right organization with the best skill set and track record; and establishing concrete objectives and ways to monitor outcomes. It takes a strong commitment, and the ability to succeed is built on trust, good communication and accountability.

LEVERAGING KNOWLEDGE AND TECHNOLOGY

For years medical practices have been concerned about stagnant reimbursement at a time when operating costs continue to increase. They often feel like they are in survival mode, and become weary with concerns about what it takes to manage the practice.

The growing intricacies of and time-consuming tasks involved in billing and optimizing collections have become burdensome to even the most sophisticated practice. It is easy to be overwhelmed by the number and type of resources needed to prudently manage the revenue cycle and maintain a profit. This is particularly evident in cognitive practices that generate less revenue than surgical specialists while seeing a higher volume of patients and having higher overhead expenses. Pediatric Partners Medical Group (PPMG) was no exception.

Seeking Solutions

In 2000, Dr. Thomas Mohr founded PPMG, a single-site practice with three physicians located northeast of San Diego. This busy practice was concerned about the inefficiencies of both the front and back office operations as it saw a steady spike in claims denials and the days in accounts receivable (DAR) climbed. Both of these indicators signaled problems with managing the revenue cycle. The practice needed a solution—an organization with the expertise and reliability to provide consistent results in revenue cycle management (RCM).

Dr. Mohr conducted research on resources that could address and resolve the practice's RCM problems. In 2001, PPMG selected athenahealth, Inc., and its Web-based practice management and billing service, athenaCollector.

Immediately upon switching to athenaCollector, the practice was able to leverage the collective billing and payer knowledge of thousands of providers using the system nationwide. Within no time, the claims denials started decreasing and the DAR was reduced by over 40%.

Gaining Comparative Advantage

Pediatric Partners was now in a position to acquire and absorb new practices. Today, the medical group has 10 locations and more than 20 physicians, and sees 86,000 patients annually. Its revenue is approaching $11 million, compared with $600,000 in 2000.

"athenahealth gave us the tools and knowledge needed for our group's brand to grow within the community, all while implementing leading workflow processes that resulted in consistent and measurable financial outcomes," states Dr. Mohr. "During our growth, we looked to implement new clinical technologies and decided to deploy a software-based [electronic health record]."

Stumbling Blocks

The practice installed software-based electronic health records (EHRs) in early 2003 at two practice locations and began to experience the typical outcomes from the traditional clinical software they purchased. Staff members went through extensive training, but shortly after going live with the EHR system they experienced growing frustration. Adding to this problem was the substantial capital investment required in both hardware and software upgrades. The practice was growing, but so were its costs. It was paying a hefty price for the decision it made.

By 2005, PPMG knew it needed to make a change and turned to athenahealth's clinical solution, athenaClinicals—a unique EHR service that is built on the same Web-based platform as its practice management system. It combines intuitive software with results-oriented services. athenaClinicals delivers improved and predictable outcomes and a solid return on investment.

Network Power and Paperless

Soon after implementing athenaClinicals, PPMG experienced more than improved clinical workflow. Using a system that combined practice management and EHRs provided easy integration of all moving parts of the practice—from scheduling to clinical task management, all in a single clinical workflow system.

There is a massive amount of paper that comes into any medical office, and with the volume in pediatrics it can be staggering. Having a centrally hosted EHR service that scans and categorizes every incoming fax, then matches clinical documents to existing patients and patient orders is an enormous time saver that improves efficiency and reduces errors. The gains are amazing. "This has given our group an incredible amount of process control on both the clinical and operational fronts, not to mention athenahealth now manages the connectivity to our labs and pharmacies, which has significantly reduced the number of calls into our practices," Dr. Mohr boasts.

By indexing inbound faxes to the correct patient (and if applicable, the original order), athenaClinicals provides the basis for enhanced closed-loop order cycle integrity.

Ready for the Future

Pediatric Partners has eliminated paper congestion while still gaining the features of a traditional EHR software system. There are continual updates to payer-specific coding rules and evaluation and management (E&M) coding reviews at the point of care. This helps providers optimize reimbursement for practice-specific, pay-for-performance payer contracts.

"athenahealth's [EHR] service is built on the same result-driven approach that allowed our group to flourish," says Dr. Mohr. "I now have real-time visibility into all of the practices, giving me the ability to manage my staff at the user level. I can access this data from anywhere."

The results Pediatric Partners have experienced have been impressive and immediate, but the practice isn't stopping there. Along with athenahealth, it is developing new order sets and templates that will allow PPMG to comply with new health plan contracts and mandates, like various consumer-directed initiatives.

This is a story of growth and success in a difficult and highly competitive environment. PPMG is a dynamic and forward-thinking medical group that will continue to maximize revenues through the clinical encounter. It is ready for a somewhat unpredictable future and prepared to take the ride.

GROWING WITH EXPERTISE

Brookhurst Ophthalmology Associates did its own practice building for years. The physicians have maintained an excellent reputation with their colleagues, who consistently sent referrals their way. Those referrals, along with referrals from patients to family and friends, became the cornerstone of the practice's growth.

Over a period of 10 years, the practice expanded from two to five physicians. The physicians were comfortable with the rate of growth and satisfied with their productivity, but things changed a couple of years ago when they experienced a change in practice economics. Three important things emerged that impacted Brookhurst Ophthalmology's financial stability:

1. New patient volume had flat-lined.
2. Reimbursement was declining.
3. Competition moved in and was aggressive in its pursuit to gain market share.

The physicians knew they needed to do something. They wanted to see more new patients, and they also wanted to offset reimbursement challenges by increasing the volume of elective services and products sold. This meant promoting both Lasik surgery and the optical department. This would require an investment in marketing. Although they knew how to build a referral-based practice, they didn't have a clue about how to market to the community.

At first they turned to Jessica Turner, their long-time practice administrator. Surely she could whip out a marketing plan and put it into motion. Jessica was straightforward in telling the physicians this didn't make sense. First, she was smart enough to know what she didn't know. She was a manager, not a marketing specialist, and didn't have the expertise to analyze market demographics about their own patients let alone a broader market. Nor did she know what would be the best return on investment for their marketing dollars.

Second, even if she had the skill set, developing a marketing plan would take away from the important aspects of her job: managing business finances, operations and staff. The physicians agreed.

The Marketing Plan

Two months later, I was called in to develop a marketing plan. The plan included detailed market research about Brookhurst's patients and the competition, and a demographic breakdown of the community catchment area. Next came learning more about the practice's strengths and weaknesses, which involved site observations, interviews with the physicians and staff, exit interviews with patients and an examination of a recently performed patient satisfaction survey.

Now we were able to develop a concrete plan, beginning with establishing defined goals for increasing new patients: Lasik elective surgery and referrals based on specific target sources. The plan outlined each marketing strategy and listed which actions were required, based on an annual budget.

The Marketing Coordinator

Once this was accomplished, it was clear that a marketing coordinator would be required to assist with implementing the plan, so a job description for this position was included with the marketing plan. Tracking tools were also recommended for accurately monitoring new patient referral sources to better understand which marketing strategies resulted in the best return on investment.

The implementation plan listed each action item with a start and target finish date and the person responsible for completing the task. The majority of the responsibilities would be handled by the new marketing coordinator, but I remained on retainer as a resource to provide advice, monitor the progress and hold people accountable for the tasks that were assigned to them.

The Results

Within 18 months, practice revenue grew by 20%, and elective procedures and new patient trends were steadily moving up. New referral sources increased by more than 38%; including physicians that had not previously referred and self-referred patients that responded to community outreach. Lasik procedures had gradually increased by 19% and are expected to continue to climb. Brookhurst Ophthalmology has no regrets about the investment it made in hiring a consultant to clarify its needs and set the practice on the right course for growth. It understands the benefits of smart-sourcing.

STRENGTH IN NUMBERS

Women's Healthcare Network (WHN) is recognized as one of the premier physician organizations in the Kansas City area. It is a formal association of nine independent OB-GYN practices in Kansas City that represents 54 physicians with practices ranging in size from a 2-physician practice up to a 12-physician group.

In the Beginning

The organization's story began in the 1990s, when managed care became a dominant force in the health insurance market. Physicians in Kansas City were feeling the squeeze. They began to recognize a growing loss of autonomy. At the same time, their practice operations were becoming more complex and costly, requiring a higher level of business expertise.

Hospitals were aligning and positioning for increased competition through mergers and acquisitions to gain strength to deal with managed care's domination. Medical practices did not have the resources to effectively respond to these forces and were slow to respond to the looming marketplace shifts.

It was clear that physicians needed to do something, but many of them were not clear about which direction to take. Physician tensions were growing, and there was a great deal of frustration as health plan contracts became more complicated. Unfortunately, many physicians were negotiating out of fear rather than from a position of strength.

Motivations to Unite

Medical practices were grounded in the desire to focus on providing quality patient care, but administrative costs to run their practices continued to escalate, and finances were becoming far more complicated. Physicians, typically not schooled in business matters, became increasingly agitated. Add to this the rising cost of malpractice insurance, and medical practices were primed to seek a solution to effectively deal with managed care without compromising their independence, their values or the quality of care they provided. Banding together for a greater presence seemed like a viable option for a number of physicians, and several physician organizations formed as a result.

Specialty Focused Network

WHN, an independent physician association, or IPA, evolved when long-established, community-leading OB-GYN medical practices joined together and began a process of developing a new company that could provide the expertise required to help support the growing business demands, including the challenges of managed care.

WHN was founded in 1996 and is owned by the member practices, although each practice continues to operate as an individual medical practice with its own federal tax ID number.

Internal Structure

WHN's organizational structure is shown in Figure 1. The Board of Directors is voted in annually with each member practice represented on the Board. This gives each practice a voice at the table. There are nine Directors, and all are physicians. The Board meets every month to discuss relevant issues and make decisions.

Administrators and practice managers have a separate meeting each month. It supports effective communication and offers an opportunity to collaborate on various operational challenges. This forum is one of WHN's fundamental strengths. The compilation of attendees represents each of the IPA partners and gives the attendees an opportunity to openly discuss issues, ideas and potential solutions to emerging problems. WHN organ-

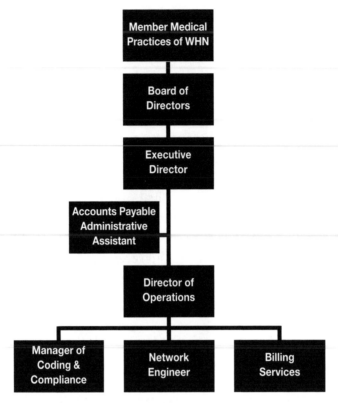

FIGURE 1. Women's Healthcare Network (WHN) organizational chart.

izes the meeting agendas including topics that may be initiated by WHN or provided by a member practice. Depending upon the agenda, either the Executive Director, Director of Operations or both may lead discussions.

WHN has 21 employees, two with senior management responsibilities.

Services Portfolio

WHN provides a range of support services, bringing a high level of commitment and expertise to member practices. These services are intended to guide and assist physician members' existing and future needs. WHN's services portfolio adjusts based on the ever-changing needs of the business requirements of its respective member practices:

- **Contracting:** WHN contracts with local health plans and manages those contracts. It also conducts a break-even analysis for the practices to help provide financial and other data-driven tools to help members make informed financial decisions that may impact their practice.

- **Billing Services:** A centralized billing office was formed in 1998 and currently processes 14,000 claims a month and manages the complete revenue cycle for the practices. The members are provided with monthly management reports to monitor performance.
- **Coding Education:** WHN recognizes that coding education and training for its members is a key element to improving practice productivity and profitability. Its training programs are led by a Certified Procedural Coder that understands both coding and compliance requirements.
- **Technology:** Information technology (IT) maintenance and support are essential components to a highly functional, evolving and integrated IT system, both internally and for the practice members. WHN's Network Engineer conducts standard monthly maintenance checks on key computer equipment at each practice site. Hardware is inventoried, monitored and, when necessary, replaced. There is a "Helpdesk" where users can report computer or application problems, and there is a "ticket" system for follow-up. WHN solves the issues either remotely or by going on-site at the practice. A field technician is dispatched to the site when needed.
- **Group Purchasing:** This program was adopted early on and continues to allow members to purchase a broad variety of services and products at a considerable savings.
- **Reporting:** WHN takes a best-practices approach to providing specialized reports and helping its members achieve higher standards of performance excellence. Benchmarking is used to create awareness and guide practice leaders in their decision-making processes. This is accomplished by looking at national data available from sources like the Medical Group Management Association, but groups also have access to comparative data about each other. The ability to compare costs, utilization and other benchmarks can aid each practice, regardless of its size.

WHN is currently working with Greenway Medical Technologies to add a dashboard tool that will be available at both the "enterprise" (corporate) and practice levels to further enhance the data reporting and benchmarking capabilities for members.

Accomplishments

For more than 12 years, WHN has explored ways to continually provide value to its member practices to encourage their success and ability to compete in a constantly changing marketplace. The services offered have provided both tangible and intangible benefits.

There have been increased opportunities to contract with several area health plans in the two-state (Kansas and Missouri) area, providing the 54-physician, multiple-clinic sites with greater market penetration and the ability to serve the needs of a larger population.

The automated appointment reminder system has increased patient compliance and reduced missed appointments, which results in improved productivity and cost savings. Previously, groups were using employees to call patients with reminders. This approach is not only labor intensive, but inefficient as calls may go unanswered. It is not uncommon for staff to have other responsibilities, so the "call process" may be interrupted or postponed due to the other needs of the practice. With the average appointment worth $120, the automated system has allowed a method for contacting hundreds of patients that may not have been previously contacted due to the limitations and costs associated with the manual system.

In its early years, WHN negotiated savings for medical malpractice insurance that resulted, in some cases, in a savings of approximately $10,000 annually per physician.

Purchasing technology by WHN resulted in considerable cost savings for hardware and software licensing. Discounts up to 60% were achieved with combined savings exceeding $500,000 for hardware and software. WHN member practices have the opportunity to enjoy the benefits of the latest technology at an affordable price.

Monthly recurring support services provided by WHN save each practice 50% of the traditional cost to accomplish these tasks. Another economic advantage is gained in the intellectual capital and benefits derived by combining resources (the knowledge and expertise of the practices and WHN) in the decision process, thus avoiding the potential for costly mistakes.

With WHN assuming responsibility for the entire RCM, specialization and efficiencies have increased, resulting in overall improved performance. In 2000, two years after WHN began its billing services, DAR averaged 53. In 2009, the average of DAR is 27. It should also be recognized that variables outside of WHN billing contributed to the decrease seen in DAR. Prompt-pay legislation and health plan payments policies also improved over this period.

The level of sophistication with the RCM provided to the members by WHN has led to increased technology acceptance by the network members and their staff. This will be a critical factor as new technologies are adapted at a local and national level, and as the government continues to place new demands and regulatory requirements on medical professionals.

Challenges

WHNs Executive Director, Gary Stanton, M.S., M.B.A., generously shared the challenges this organization faces—many of which are resolved through constructive and collaborative efforts:

1. **Recognizing varying group cultures with nine independent practices that vary in size and operating philosophies:** This can contribute to delays or create conflicts among members.
2. **Sustaining measurable economic gains:** The practices generally operate with low overhead, and WHN services represent a line item expense. Since WHN is a cost to each practice, it continually has the need to overcome the "What have you done for me lately?" mindset of the practices.
3. **Keeping a common focus:** Physicians are busy, and each practice has its own share of business challenges. It can be difficult to get nine practices moving together in sync and sharing a common focus.
4. **Contracting:** WHN uses the messenger model for contracting, with WHN acting as the go-between for the practice and the plan, which is not the most efficient method, but is necessary under WHN's current business model.

Staying Ahead of the Curve

Last year, WHN implemented a new practice management system and purchased the EHR module. Every member of WHN now uses the same practice management system for appointment scheduling, financials and reporting.

Initially, three of the practices also implemented the EHR application, but more are expected to come on board. Armed with this integrated technology, practices are evaluating workflow patterns and redesigning internal systems that will add more efficiency to operations, reduce steps, eliminate paper copies of information and improve the patient care experience. In time, WHN physicians will be able to use this technological advantage to measure and report clinical outcomes.

"To say the implementation of the new [practice management system] and [EHR] did not have its share of challenges would be misleading. After the largest practice became deployed (about mid-year), the network began to show signs of strain," states Stanton. There were adjustments to the new system, and performance complaints emerged.

Practices not on the new system became more reluctant to implement it, and tensions increased. WHN brought in an outside IT company to work with the in-house staff. Over the course of several weeks, a process unfolded to troubleshoot issues and take needed action. As each fix was accomplished, confidence grew, and the practices became more satisfied throughout the network.

WHN has faced many challenges, but has demonstrated its ability to take action on those challenges. As a result, WHN is strategically positioned in the local healthcare market.

The Facts

- WHN was founded in 1996 and is a private, limited liability company located in Lenexa, Kansas.
- It is owned by nine medical practices with 54 OB-GYN physicians and 16 clinics in the Kansas City metropolitan area.
- WHN employs a staff of 21.
- Chairman of the Board is Richard Gutknecht, M.D.
- Executive Director is Gary Stanton, M.S., M.B.A.
- Director of Operations is Mary Lynn Thomas.

Opportunity Knocks

A physician network provides a significant opportunity for community physicians to strengthen their resources, identify opportunities and gain business intelligence. Networks vary in their complexities and in their ability to expand their portfolio of services and respond to both market shifts and the changing needs and goals of their physician members. It takes a strong executive director and committed physician leadership to manage all the variables, demands and political shifts that may occur with any health services organization.

BUSINESS DEMANDS

It's not business as usual. The demands of competitive forces, a challenging economy, new technology and government pressures require a new focus for medical practices. Keeping up with both the business and the clinical side of medicine is difficult.

The continually changing business needs of managing a practice require a higher level of business acumen. Physicians need to understand how to analyze the key performance indicators that will keep them informed about the practice's position and enable them to make wise decisions that will strategically position them for the future. Acquiring these skills seems unaffordable for medical practices that struggle to keep profits from declining.

Physicians are beginning to recognize that the price of obtaining expertise on the business side of the practice often provides a good return on investment—whether it's analyzing business performance and finances, examining operations, developing a strategic plan or crafting a customized marketing plan. The operational needs and cost of staffing to meet those needs means you must use staff wisely. Streamlining processes and smart-sourcing some functions can often be an affordable alternative to managing staff cost. It's certainly worthwhile to spend a little time exploring what opportunities exist to smart-source some of the practice functions. There's a broad scope of services to consider—everything from laundry to various business and technology processes.

If smart-sourcing can provide you with a higher level of expertise at a reduced cost, it makes sense, as long as you communicate well and monitor performance. It's still your practice so you still need to make sure reporting requirements are satisfactory to hold your smart-source business partners accountable.

THE SECRETS

1. Explore opportunities to smart-source when the practice needs additional support.
2. Leveraging talent and technology can strengthen your position and improve outcomes.
3. Don't overtax the administrator when major projects require more time and a different skill set.
4. There is strength in numbers.
5. Smart-sourcing offers professional resources that can save the practice money.
6. The keys to smart-sourcing are communication, relationship building and accountability.

CHAPTER 14

Starting Over: Yes You Can!

Years ago, the majority of physicians completed their residency and found a place to hang their shingle, use their stethoscope and enjoy a dedicated career and stable practice. Not so today; things are a lot different now, and some physicians experience disappointment or disenchantment early in their careers. Some grapple with whether they should be employed or have their own practice. Managed care challenges make their choices even more difficult.

> **KEY FACT:** *When things just aren't working out, there are options to improve your professional life.*

Physicians frustrated with where they are and, perhaps, the practice choice they made sometimes feel trapped. Others just want to bail out and look for a completely different career path; but this usually doesn't make much sense for physicians that feel destined to practice medicine and have made an enormous investment in their education and training.

This chapter highlights three physicians who share their personal experiences. They found themselves in difficult situations that led them to search for something different. They will talk about the reasons behind their desire to make a major change in their professional career. You will learn about the processes they went through and the challenges they faced, and how the changes they made affected their lives. Their stories are unique, but all three have something in common—they were willing to take a risk that changed for the better their professional life as a physician.

FROM COAST TO COAST

Brent Greenberg, M.D., is a primary care physician who spent most of his life in San Diego. He chose family practice because he liked the global treatment of patients. His career game plan was to join a primary care practice in the San Diego area so he would be near his family. While he was in his residency in Chicago, he began his search for an opportunity, exploring several practices in the San Diego area. There were two practices he considered joining. One was a younger practice that seemed cutting-edge, was politically active in family practice in San Diego, was composed of subspecialty physicians and was more academically based. The other was a practice that had been in existence for 40 years and was more traditional. With significant student loans to consider, he selected the older practice with a lower buy-in, immediate production bonuses and partnership after one year, joining Penn Elm Medical Group in Escondido, California, in 1997.

First Practice

He was very happy at Penn Elm, which was composed of seven or eight physicians at the time. His partners were supportive and gave him the flexibility to run his own schedule. The group entered into a contractual insurance agreement with Scripps within a short time after he arrived and were full-risk as a single-specialty private medical group. Things were fairly smooth for awhile, and the practice was expanding and thriving.

But by 2002, the tides were changing, and San Diego became a more challenging medical environment, not only for Penn Elm, but for all medical groups throughout southern California. Reimbursements were decreasing, and government intervention was increasing. Dr. Greenberg began to work longer hours just to maintain the same life style. The economics of family medicine seemed dismal, and he was becoming frustrated and concerned.

Shifting Sands

He attended a national meeting in 2005 in San Francisco and heard a lecture on the future of family medicine. As he listened to these healthcare leaders giving their advice, he soon realized these were things he was already trying, like adopting electronic health records (EHRs), adding ancillaries and getting into cosmetics. It helped a little, but overall it wasn't working. Sure, EHRs had made a significant difference in improving efficiency and resulted in a cost savings of more than $20,000 a month, but he certainly didn't believe EHRs were the saving grace that would protect his financial future in family medicine.

Dr. Greenberg wasn't hearing long-term solutions for family medicine. "My feeling was that I'm in a specialty that for at least the next decade (if not 20 years) is going to be riding some very low waves before it swings back," Greenberg told me. "I was at an age where I just couldn't take more risk. I had student loans to pay off and a young family." He was 38 years old and struggling not only financially, but with major concerns about his future in medicine. He was discouraged. "The only time I enjoyed my practice was when I was caring for my patients," he said.

Dr. Greenberg was seeking opportunities to improve his financial picture. He and one of his partners from Penn Elm opened an aesthetic medical practice to provide cosmetic care and supplement their income, but he soon discovered he was not cut out for retail medicine. "It just wasn't gratifying when compared to caring for patients with real medical conditions," he explained.

Around this same time, a long-time friend from medical school visited Dr. Greenberg. This friend had a vein practice in Greensboro, North Carolina, and was in town attending a conference. Greenberg joined him at the conference and began to analyze the field of vein treatment. "These are happy patients with complex conditions, and it would be gratifying to treat them," he thought.

Reaction

Dr. Greenberg reacted and was a bit naïve when in 2007 he joined a San Diego-based vein treatment center that was treating "cash basis" patients. This was a different model of vein treatment than his friend's practice, which contracted with insurance companies to provide vein care. As if the economics of medicine weren't tough enough for Dr. Greenberg, by 2008 the challenges of a cash-based practice in San Diego during a major national economic downturn made it impossible for his vein practice to survive. By September 2008, after doing all that he could to save it, he shut down the vein practice. During this difficult time, his friend suggested he come to Greensboro to join his vein practice. In January 2009, Brent Greenberg did just that.

A Great Decision

Moving to the Greensboro practice has been a great choice for Dr. Greenberg and his family. The cost of living is far lower than in San Diego, and he's in a niche market that works. They are seeing some patients out of network, but the practice is growing and doing well.

What advice does this young physician have for others that are feeling insecure and frustrated in their current setting, and concerned about their future? This is what Brent Greenberg has learned:

1. You shouldn't just hope things will get better by doing the same thing. You need to respond to the current environment. When things change in your world, don't wait for something to happen.
2. It's important to expand your skills to make yourself marketable, have more options and discover ways to find a better quality of life.
3. There are other places in the world where you can live and work.

Uprooting his family and moving across the country was hard in the beginning, but Dr. Greenberg is happy, noting, "I'm home for dinner, I can go to the gym, I have fewer financial worries and love what I do." This was a major move for this young family, but Dr. Greenberg has no regrets. His family life style has improved, and he has a sense of financial stability at last. He is seeing happy patients with complex conditions, and it is gratifying.

SETTING A NEW COURSE

Mark Logan, M.D., left an OB-GYN residency in the early 1980s when he discovered how much he enjoyed the emergency department while moonlighting for extra money. After practicing emergency medicine for 16 years in rural Vermont, he was grandfathered in to sit for the boards and become board certified. He eventually moved to the southwest and stayed for 10 years, but for personal reasons that were particularly difficult, he left emergency medicine and returned to Vermont. He was in his early 50s, and he was setting a new course for his career.

What Next?

Dr. Logan had great empathy for people struggling with addictions, so after a short stint at Dartmouth Hitchcock Medical Center, working as a project coordinator, he decided to set up a practice in addiction medicine. Within 4 to 5 months, his Rutland, Vermont, practice was seeing 25 to 30 patients a day. "I was doing everything myself, including my own billing. It practically became a 24/7 job," Dr. Logan told me. "To save my sanity, I hired Jennifer Rogers to manage the practice."

In January 2008, Dr. Logan took over an existing primary care practice, Green Mountain Family Medicine. This was a good-sized family practice, and he merged it with the addiction services. It has grown beyond anything he had imagined. There are now two nurse practitioners, three nurses, an addiction coordinator and administrative support staff for a total of nine employees. Obviously, he is providing much needed services to the area.

Versatility Reigns

Dr. Logan is pursuing a fellowship with the University of Arizona in integrative medicine. He founded another practice entity: Sanctuary Integrative Medicine. This is housed in a separate facility and offers homeopathy, naturopathy, functional medicine, massage therapy and traditional Chinese medicine.

Dr. Logan is renovating an old farmhouse and will have a 2,500 square foot facility. It is the original Rutland Mahoney Farm from which land was used to build the Rutland Regional Medical Center in the 1940s. "I've really branched out with a passion to help people through the use of different treatment modalities that have typically been ignored by traditional medicine. I am even teaching Kripalu yoga dance to patients and colleagues as a part of the practice."

His rapid and continual growth has all been by word of mouth, and although Rutland is a community of about 12,000 people, patients travel from other regions to come to this unique practice.

At age 58, Dr. Logan is excited about his practice and his future. Perhaps his biggest challenge will be to keep up with the business and administrative needs of the practice with its burgeoning growth.

FROM SURVIVAL TO SUCCESS

Psychiatrist Edward Freeman, M.D., had a private practice in the Houston, Texas, metro area and worked out of two facilities—one in Clearlake and one in Missouri City. He needed to supplement his income as he experienced the financial pressures of the managed care environment. So he started taking a 45-minute flight to the Rio Grande Valley where there was a high need for his services, and he worked out of a small family medicine clinic that managed the business side of his practice. He was doing well for over four years. Then in 2003, he discovered there were ethical issues with management of the clinic that would compromise his integrity if he stayed. He left, and soon after, everything collapsed financially for him.

Dr. Freeman could not turn his efforts into capital in the existing managed care climate and was unable to support his young family. He was even doing locum tenens work with a government mental health clinic in Rio Grande just to stay afloat.

Facing Reality

Things quickly became more difficult financially, so Dr. Freeman and his wife started thinking about leaving the state. They needed to do something in order to survive. Then he received a direct mail flyer from a recruiter. "This was the first and last direct mail I ever responded to," he said emphatically. The recruiter represented Metroplex Hospital/Scott & White, in Killeen, Texas, a town with fewer than 100,000 people that was also home to Fort Hood, the largest U.S. Army facility in the world. After speaking with the recruiter, Dr. Freeman decided to explore the opportunity.

A Smart Decision

He interviewed with the hospital and talked to other psychiatrists in the area. The number one reason Dr. Freeman chose to go forward with the Killeen opportunity was the office manager of the practice he would be affiliated with, Patrick O Brien, was obviously skilled and knowledgeable and knew how to work with managed care insurance companies. "I knew he would help me succeed, and he has. The practice is exploding!," Dr. Freeman told me. He is seeing 80 to 85 new patients among his 350 to 400 patient visits each month.

The hospital gave Dr. Freeman a one-year income guarantee, but he was self sufficient within six months. "I had forgotten the gold mine of opportunity that exists in small towns in Texas, in fact throughout the United States. It's been great to be in a small town; we do many more family things than we did in Houston," Dr. Freeman told me. They recently built a new home on five acres of land and really enjoy it. "Of course, it's a trade off. You give up some of the advantages of living in a big city, but Austin is only 35 miles away," he said.

Life Is Good

Dr. Freeman's wife, Tamara, has gone through her own career change. When the children, now ages 10 and 11, were born, she gave up her career as a biologist at UT Medical Center and became a pastry chef. Their move to Killeen gave her an opportunity to open her order-only pastry business. They recently purchased a full-service bakery, Sweet Eats, and are completely renovating it. Life is good for the Freeman family; they are happy.

OPPORTUNITY KNOCKS

I thank these three physicians for so generously sharing their stories with me and allowing you an opportunity to take a glimpse at what they experienced and how it changed their lives. Hopefully, most of you are perfectly happy where you are, whether you are a physician, allied health professional or healthcare executive. But the real message here is that we always have choices. It's a matter of opening the door and looking at what is on the other side, being willing to step outside our comfort zone when things aren't going well and to explore potential opportunities. There are no guarantees and, certainly, there are plenty of risks. But these enlightening stories are testimony that, indeed, opportunity knocks.

IT'S NOT EASY

After spending years practicing medicine and making an investment in the practice and getting comfortable in a community, it isn't easy to start over. Leaving behind everything familiar can be very difficult. But as Dr. Greenberg said, "There are other places in the world where you can live and work." And he is also right when he said, "You shouldn't just hope things will get better by doing the same thing." In reality, we all have choices, some more difficult than others.

THE SECRETS

1. It's important to recognize when you are in a *no-win* situation.
2. Change only occurs when you are willing to change.
3. You need to maintain a positive attitude and an adventurous spirit.
4. People can make major changes at different times in their career.

CHAPTER 15

The Practice of the Future

W ho can predict how medical practices will function in the future? Certainly not me—I don't have a crystal ball or a stash of fortune cookies in the cupboard, and I don't profess to read palms or tea leaves. Nonetheless, I do believe there are a few obvious changes we can expect to impact medical practices in the near future. These changes center on measuring and managing quality of services and care; focusing on employees' expectations and needs; and advancing the level of technology.

> **KEY FACT:** *Healthcare executives and physicians must be proactive to influence changes that affect the future of their practice.*

THE QUALITY FACTOR

Quality plays an important role in improving outcomes through increased efficiency, reducing errors and controlling the cost of healthcare. The focus on quality has increased considerably over the past 10 years, and the commitment to improve quality will continue.

The U.S. Department of Health and Human Services Agency for Healthcare Research and Quality prepares an annual report on healthcare disparity, based on studies involving the quality of and access to healthcare for different segments of the population.

The National Committee for Quality Assurance (NCQA), a private, not-for-profit organization, is dedicated to improving healthcare quality. The NCQA provides quality oversight and improvement initiatives at all levels of the healthcare system. The NCQA prepares an annual report: *The State of Health Care Quality.* The 13th annual report, for the year 2009, available at www.ncqa.org, provides extensive, very specific information on performance data and how key measures of clinical quality continue to improve each year. This is a trend that we can expect to continue from year to year.

Of interest, in the 9th annual report the NCQA stated that it is not coincidental that the latest performance gains were recorded in a year that saw broad acceptance of two important and complementary improvement strategies: paying for quality and physician- and hospital-level performance measurement. These two strategies have been incorporated into mainstream efforts to improve care and prevent complications. The pay-for-performance concept approaches offering incentives based on performance. The incentives can be financial or the promise of added recognition in a provider directory. These efforts are diverse, ranging from government-sponsored to health-plan-specific initiatives.

The NCQA's Quality Plus standards are designed to recognize and reward cutting-edge organizations that meet tough new standards in the areas of Member Connections, and Care Management and Health Improvement. These standards focus on promoting wellness and prevention.

Health insurers also have internal programs to measure quality and identify physicians that provide higher quality care (i.e., access to care, continuity of care, utilization, patient satisfaction, outcomes). They develop their own report cards and gather data from various sources including claims and patient surveys.

These are just a few of the entities that are reviewing and analyzing healthcare quality and looking at different performance measures. The focus on quality is obvious and promises to be even more prominent in the future.

Customer Service Takes Center Stage

Patient satisfaction is moving to the forefront. According to Robert Wolosin of Press Ganey, a consulting firm that specializes in healthcare satisfaction measurement and improvement, in his article "Role of Patient Satisfaction" in the December 2003 edition of *Physician's News Digest*, "analysts expect greater attention and scrutiny to be given to the accountability function of patient satisfaction scores, and to ways in which patient satisfaction measurement can be further integrated into an overall measure of clinical quality." For some time now, a number of HMOs have rewarded physician groups using health outcomes and patient satisfaction information.

Patients are also beginning to conduct research when choosing their physicians. They go online and seek information about a specific physician through a search engine. They also investigate doctors by going to the medical practice's website. Beyond this, patients are able to look at a physician's past performance by obtaining a report like the Physician Quality Report produced by HealthGrades and available with the click of a mouse.

These studies and actions are all evidence of a continued and growing commitment to improve healthcare quality. This includes an increased focus on the expectations of healthcare providers and establishing sound techniques that address increased accountability within the practice.

It is wise for physicians to measure patient satisfaction so they can objectively assess how patients view their experience in the practice. Patient encounter interviews will rate the individual patient visit, and, as with all satisfaction measurement, are best performed by a specialist that is not employed in the practice. A more common method to measure satisfaction is a written patient survey that is completed anonymously and sent to a third party to be tallied and analyzed. A sample survey form has been added to the Toolbox.

Measuring Quality

Physicians and administrators need to establish methods to monitor quality within the medical office. It's not enough to say quality is a priority, it must be demonstrated by integrating quality performance measures into the medical practice. According to Bryan P. Bergeron, M.D., in an article entitled "Performance Management in Small Practices" in the March/April 2005 issue of the *The Journal of Medical Practice Management*,® "Someone in the practice must decide which indicators to monitor; establish acceptable ranges of indicator values; analyze the data; and act on their analysis. The very process of making these decisions is a major component of performance management." He further states, "It's important to use a mix of clinical and non-clinical indicators to assure inevitable clinical problems are addressed."

The government is involved in programs that will expand its ability to obtain information about each medical practice to monitor quality performance and develop standards of care. Physicians are already experiencing the government and insurance industry's push for increasing outcome measurements and evidenced-based approaches to providing medical care that is expected to improve quality and reduce costs.

Quality Improves Profits

Quality measurements will continue to expand in both the clinical and business aspects of the practice. Office operations must be evaluated, and practices need to commit to reducing processes, eliminating waste and duplication, and reducing errors. These are important factors in controlling the costs of running a medical practice.

Six Sigma is a business management strategy that seeks to improve the quality of processes by removing error and minimizing variability, using a set of quality management and statistical methods and following a defined sequence of steps with quantifiable targets. In the book *Lean Six Sigma for the Medical Practice* (Greenbranch Publishing, 2009), the authors Frank Cohen and Owen Dahl state, "Improving profitability by improving process is not just a concept; it's a mandate for medical providers and their staff. Even more than that, it's a moral imperative."

Improvement in quality provides an added advantage of increasing patient, staff and physician satisfaction. Demonstrated quality will also influence a medical group's ability to remain competitive. Physicians that make the commitment to quality and exhibit that commitment can be a driving force in improving the quality of healthcare services.

BUSINESS INTELLIGENCE

Medical practices and large clinics must take on the strategic planning approach of other businesses by making decisions based on extensive research and comprehensive data collection and analysis. This is often referred to as "gathering business intelligence." Too often, medical businesses in the past have relied on instincts and basic internal data to make decisions about their future. The information presented in Table 1 shows the importance of business intelligence in shaping the future of medical practices.

Gathering and responding to business intelligence is essential for medical practices and other medical businesses that want to remain strong and compete effectively in the future. It will help to improve performance by resolving emerging issues that may pose a threat to the business, and by setting realistic goals and implementing strategies to strengthen the practices' position in the market. In reality, you must measure practice performance and examine influencing factors to manage the business better.

TABLE 1. Business Intelligence Matrix

Situational awareness	Filtering out irrelevant information and synthesizing the relevant data
Risk assessment	Weighing current and future risk, the cost and benefit, and discovering what plausible actions might be taken and when
Decision support	Using information wisely, providing warning of important events so preventive steps can be taken
Purpose of business intelligence	Helping business leaders analyze and make better decisions thus improving sales, profitability, customer satisfaction and/or staff morale

If you fail to do so you risk making poor decisions because:
- There will be a lack of objective findings;
- Too little essential knowledge about your true position and past business performance; and
- Without this information, there is a strong likelihood of compromising the results.

The mantra "You must measure to manage," so often stated, is wise advice to strengthening business performance, remaining competitive and responding effectively to both internal and external shifts in the medical care and business environment.

THE MEDICAL HOME

The medical home, also referred to as the patient-centered medical home, is defined as an approach to providing comprehensive medical care. It is designed to facilitate partnership between individual patients and their personal physicians. This is an ambitious care model that has emerged in recent years after being introduced by the American Academy of Pediatrics in 1967.

Since that time, several projects have worked on enhancing this model; and in 2007, the American Academy of Family Physicians, the American Academy of Pediatrics, American College of Physicians and American Osteopathic Association—the leading primary care physician organizations in the United States—released the list of joint principles of the patient-centered medical home. The list focuses on ways to improve patient care and outcomes in a current system that is fragmented and lacks the ability to expedite decision-making through shared information. The list is available online at en.wikipedia.org/wiki/Medical_home.

Among the principles is the fact that payment must appropriately recognize the added value provided to patients who have a patient-centered medical home and reflect the value that falls outside the face-to-face visit. The medical home physician will be assuming a considerable amount of responsibility, and determining the value of this will be a challenge.

As of mid-2009, it was reported that 22 pilot projects involving medical homes were being conducted in 14 states. The projects are evaluating factors such as clinical quality, cost, patient experience/satisfaction and provider experience/satisfaction. Primary concerns for this model are:

1. How the home physician will be compensated;
2. The current inability to share medical information across the continuum of care and;
3. The sophisticated information technology (IT) within the medical community that does not exist in many medical practices today, especially solo and small group practices.

If the patient-centered model matures and is supported with proper financial compensation for the medical home physician, patients will love it. Only time will tell if this model emerges as a long-term viable model of care and a solution to the fragmentation of care and the patient frustration that currently exist.

THE WORKFORCE

The healthcare industry is likely to continue experiencing enormous challenges in recruiting and managing the workforce. These challenges are like shifting sands: some are the result of the current economic and political situation; others have been a concern for years, such as the nursing shortage.

The Younger Worker

When Generation Y (1981–2000) entered the workforce, they forever changed the employment landscape for both employers and staff. Physicians, physician leaders and office managers must pay close attention to human resources, being both flexible and open-minded, while at the same time setting clear expectations regarding job performance for Gen Y staffers.

These younger employees have wants and needs that are broader than those of employees of the past. They have different expectations and sometimes question authority. They want to know why something must be done a certain way and need to be convinced before they willingly accept change.

These employees present new challenges and expect managers to earn their loyalty.

Younger workers—the Gen Yers—cannot remember a time when they didn't have immediate access to information and communication. They became adults in an electronic and instant world—the Internet, blogging, text messaging and social networking. It's no wonder their expectations are different.

Talk to Me

When it comes to the work environment, the expectations are very real, and a medical office is no exception. These employees want to know how they are doing at work, and they want to know *now!*

Feedback is vital to this younger generation. It's incredibly important for them to know how their work is perceived and the impact it's having—especially those that are ambitious and will be our future leaders. This is forcing healthcare managers around the country to rethink how they discuss employee performance. The annual review for feedback just won't cut it anymore.

At a corporate level, changes in dealing with younger employees are already taking shape. A few years ago, Ernst and Young launched an online "Feedback Zone," where employees can request or submit feedback at any time. Not a bad concept—it's responsive, paperless and fast. They also incorporated a mentor program, assigning each employee a mentor. That would be more burdensome for a medical office with fewer than 10 employees.

According to Ernst and Young, as cited in the article by Brittany Hite entitled "Employers Rethink How They Give Feedback" in *The Wall Street Journal* on October 13, 2008, 65% of Gen Y workers indicated that detailed guidance in daily work was moderately to extremely important, and 85% said they want frequent and *candid* performance feedback. In other words, "don't paint a pretty picture—tell me the truth, and give me help where I don't measure up." Beyond this, they are still seeking the proverbial pat on the back when they've done well. Don't wait for the annual review.

What Can You Do?

It may seem like keeping Gen Y motivated and happy will be high-maintenance, but staying in touch isn't all that difficult, and keeping employees motivated and happy is critical to staff productivity and longevity.

First of all, be clear in communicating your expectations, especially when it comes to training, and give frequent feedback. If there is a change in performance (good or bad), be timely in addressing it. When it comes to instant responses, keep communication clear, loose and brief. Finally, hone your listening skills by getting employees' feedback and reading their body language.

There's a new generation of worker alright, but it may be just a different approach to what most workers really want. Other generations have not felt empowered to ask or sometimes demand feedback, but they still want it—it's good communication, and it's helpful to both the employee and the boss.

Gen Yers are more vocal about their needs. They ask for what they want, and they expect to get it. And most are willing to work for it. After all, they grew up in a world where everyone gets a trophy, and Mom and Dad always told them they were *special*.

Resources and Creativity

Large corporations have resources to analyze the differences in employees and explore ways to meet the needs of new generations. Smaller employers, such as medical practices, compete for these employees without the resources of big industry. I believe physicians and administrators will face continued challenges in their efforts to recruit and retain skilled and dedicated employees. It may require expanding the realm of what they offer for employees. It may require looking outside the profession to recruit business personnel and providing more extensive training about the inner workings of a medical office—and more specifically, their own practice.

Medical practice leaders need to be more creative to identify opportunities to attract and retain staff. Look for perks you can offer employees that are mutually beneficial. For example, the practice can offer preventive health programs on site and partially pay the membership dues for staff to join a local health club. By doing this, the practice becomes a more competitive employer and encourages a healthier staff, which may in the end affect its healthcare insurance premiums. It also happens to provide an endorsement of the practice's commitment to better health. This is just one example of what might be expected in the future. Business managers should continually seek ways to unite with employees in a meaningful way that improves business performance and places increased value on employees.

Staffing for Technology

IT also changes what we need and expect from employees. The medical practice already dependent on its computer will find its needs and usage expanding. Beyond collecting and moving data electronically, it will be called upon to store and manage even more data as it moves through the age of technology. Some medical practices have already prepared for this by creating a key position of IT Manager, or for the smaller practice an IT Coordinator.

The medical office of the future must have as its internal point person someone with a keen understanding of the practice's IT system—someone that assumes responsibility for keeping the systems up and running and managing the electronic information. This person is integral to working effectively with external software and hardware support services and building a strong relationship that serves the practice in keeping the IT system humming.

THE PHYSICIAN SHORTAGE

It's interesting to me how seldom I hear anyone talk about the physician shortage, yet it not only exists but continues to grow and is likely to be exacerbated by healthcare reform. As a patient, a mother, a grandmother and a concerned citizen, I find it alarming.

Many primary care physicians around the country are at capacity and are not accepting new patients or are opting out of Medicare. Some are choosing to focus on elective services or develop a concierge practice that limits the number of patients, but ensures each patient will get more of the physician's time for a set, agreed-upon annual fee. Scheduling an appointment with some specialists requires a wait of three to four weeks (and even longer in some areas of the United States) unless it is declared urgent by the referring physician.

How Real Is It?

The physician shortage is definitely real and is expected to get even worse.

According to a June 20, 2009, article in the *Washington Post* titled "Primary-Care Doctor Shortage May Undermine Reform Efforts," by Ashley Halsey III, fixing the problem will require fundamental change in medical education and compensation to lure more doctors into primary care. The article states that the American Academy of Family Physicians predicts that if current trends continue, the shortage of family doctors will reach 40,000 in little more than 10 years.

It will be difficult to attract medical students to choose a career in primary care when they can enjoy a far greater income as a specialist. According to the *Post* article, recent data compiled by Merritt Hawkins, a medical recruiting firm, shows the average income for family physicians is $173,000, while oncologists earn $335,000, radiologists $391,000 and cardiologists $419,000.

The nation is getting older and so are its physicians. Many of them are expected to retire within the next 10 years, and younger physicians just aren't willing to work as hard. This further exacerbates the physician shortage across the specialties. When these trusted, aging physicians retire, their patients will be at a loss to find a new physician, especially in primary care.

The physician shortage will certainly continue to impact physicians' ability to meet the demands placed on them by patient volume. It may be a call for more physicians to consider adding a mid-level provider to the practice to ensure patient access and guarantee that care is not compromised.

THE HIGH-TECH WORLD

The use of technology in the medical practice is continually evolving and may have seemingly limitless potential. Savvy physicians and administrators continually explore opportunities to increase the use of technology. They understand its importance in improving efficiency and reducing costly variables that ultimately compromise outcomes, service and profitability.

Electronic health records (EHRs) provide a powerful tool to help medical practices extract, analyze and manage data. They are an integral part of evidence-based medicine, reducing errors, measuring quality and building accountability into the healthcare system not only for providers, but to ensure patients are compliant, which can contribute significantly to improving quality.

Political forces have moved to the forefront in persuading physicians to implement cost-saving EHR technology that is expected to improve clinical outcomes and the continuity of clinical care across the continuum of care. This, of course, is expected to provide government with the ability (through data-mining) to better monitor clinical performance.

Solo and small-group practices and physicians close to retirement who have been hesitant to adopt EHRs in the past have declared the investment too costly and have been concerned about the difficulty in adapting their existing records and learning a new system. However, with government applying more pressure, offering financial incentives for implementing and *meaningful* application of EHRs and eventually penalizing noncompliant physicians, the need to implement an EHR system becomes paramount to these smaller practices.

It will be important for physicians planning to implement an EHR system to take a rational approach and not be reactive. It would be advantageous to hire a consultant with IT skills in the medical practice setting—someone with specific experience helping medical practices through the selection, planning and implementation process.

Healthcare leaders are working toward the goal of an integrated EHR system that allows physicians to access patient healthcare information across the continuum of care to expedite and improve medical care and outcomes and, over time, reduce costs.

Clinical Applications

Technology has made major strides in the development of a vast array of diagnostic tools that save time and facilitate the early detection and intervention of a number of diseases. These rapid improvements in technology sometimes result in equipment becoming outdated before it is even paid for, making the investment in technology more challenging.

Computers and advanced technology are also changing the way physicians perform surgery, making procedures safer and less invasive. Some surgeons are now completing surgical procedures with the use of a surgical cart—the robot—while seated at a console viewing three-dimensional images of the surgical area of the patient. This is just the beginning of how technology will advance the field of medicine and change how healthcare professionals are trained, how they are evaluated and what they must do to keep their skills current.

Medical residents are now learning both cognitive and surgical techniques in a way unimaginable 20 years ago. It is expected that advancements in technology will continue to change the training of future physicians and improve outcomes. The operating room of the future will be quite different from those of the past.

Technology will permeate the medical practice of the future, from how business aspects are managed to the quality of care provided to patients. Patients that at one time needed to obtain their medical records from multiple sources will eventually have access to an electronic copy of their complete health record. This record will follow them through the healthcare system, regardless of where they seek medical care.

Technology moves information accurately and swiftly, at a speed that increases demand and changes expectations. Technology leads the way in improving precision with both clinical and business processes, and will continue to offer improved applications for the business of medicine and the delivery of healthcare.

ON THE HORIZON

Things constantly change, and new concepts emerge that affect the way we think and the way we act. Certainly healthcare reform will continue to be at the forefront with concerns about the impact of how reform shapes up, when it will be enacted and how it will be implemented. Younger physicians will respond differently to these issues than their peers that are 50 or older.

I hesitate to mention what might be next with such a plethora of thoughts that come to my mind. But here are a couple of other things we see popping up that might play a bigger role in your future.

Patient Centered

Medicine is in an age that redefines the influence of patient perceptions (of their medical care) and how this affects market share and physician reimbursement. Patients are more informed than ever before thanks to the Internet. It is also an era of transparency, making it possible for patients to distinguish between average and good care. All these things are likely to result in more patient-centric care.

What does this mean? It means a greater burden will be placed on physicians to deliver care that meets patients' expectations, as well as delivering the desired clinical outcome. It may also mean that hospitals are likely to recognize the need to work with their medical staff to create a service excellence strategy to achieve and sustain higher levels of patient satisfaction in the hospital.

Press Ganey, a leader in healthcare improvement solutions, has worked with hospitals across the country, including a number of high-profile organizations. Press Ganey has developed a Physician Partnership program as a new approach to building stronger alliances for mutual success. Its brochure on this subject states: "Physician Partnership is created when physicians are both satisfied and engaged with the hospital. Partnership seeks to satisfy their expectations for basics, such as excellence of care, while engaging their hearts and minds through communication, trust, and aligned incentives."

I absolutely agree with this. If hospitals could meet this need, they would have the potential to expand physician trust, strengthen the relationship and create a powerful partnership. Such a relationship would benefit patients and the medical community, and result in better management of healthcare resources.

Eco-Friendly

Environmental issues are getting the nation's attention. We will see more eco-friendly products being offered and articles written discussing how to reduce waste in the office. More medical practices are likely to take a con-scientious look at how they can improve the ecologic landscape by thought-ful use of resources and "going green." The reduction of waste results in reducing costs, and using recyclable products is smart business.

Online Patient Care

We may see a surge in patient visits online, as some insurers begin paying for digital diagnoses. An article in the June 30, 2009, issue of *The Wall Street Journal*, penned by Anna Wilde Mathews, entitled "The Doctor Will Text You Now," discusses this topic. "If this service is valued, and there is payment for it, we will see many more primary-care physicians doing it," said Ted Epperly, a doctor in Boise, Idaho, who is president of the American Academy of Family Physicians. He stated that he is offering online visits.

The article stated that online care, although not widely used, is growing as more health insurers begin paying doctors for treating patients virtu-ally. Aetna, Inc., and Cigna Corp. are covering digital visits, albeit at a lower fee. Blue Cross Blue Shield plans to cover these visits in some states, and both WellPoint, Inc., and Humana, Inc., are trying it in parts of the coun-try and may expand their coverage.

Online visits may appeal to more patients in the future, based on the looming physician shortage. We are definitely seeing more physicians offering e-mail to patients and enjoying the ability to get information to and from patients without tying up the phone lines.

IT'S YOUR FUTURE

The future of the medical practice may not be predictable, but it is guar-anteed to be exciting. These are revolutionary times for physicians and healthcare executives.

The focus on quality; a new and different employee workforce; the alarming concern over the physician shortage and reimbursement issues; the rapid advancement of technology; and the government's watchful eye will certainly change the outlook of the medical practice. The secret to your success will depend on *you* also keeping a watchful eye and being prepared to act when practice stability is threatened. Step boldly into the future, one step at a time.

THE SECRETS

1. The nation's focus on healthcare quality is reality.
2. Your commitment to healthcare quality must be demonstrated with objective outcome measures.
3. Business intelligence is a critical component to business success.
4. Retaining dedicated employees requires more effort and creativity than in the past.
5. The application of technology is essential to improving medical practice efficiency.
6. The physician shortage poses a potential threat to medical practices, hospitals and the consumer.

FORM ADDED TO YOUR TOOLBOX:

☞ *Patient Satisfaction Survey*

Index

(Page numbers followed by "f" denote figures; those followed by "t" denote tables.)

S

T

Your "Toolbox" forms
in PDF and Word
are available online at:
http://capko.greenbranch.com
Code: G4E15C

Download Toolbox Forms at http://capko.greenbranch.com
Access code printed on page 218 of this book.

TOOLBOX FORMS

Alpha Numerical Accuracy Quiz
Appointment Power Words Matrix (Chapter 5)
Batch Control Slip
Charting Do's and Don'ts
Clinical Telephone Tracking Incoming Calls (Chapter 3)
Communication Matrix (Chapter 6)
Comparing Key Performance Indicators
Don't Ask These Questions
Employee Benefits Audit Form
Employee Counseling Form
Employee Exit Interview
Employment Agreement Letter
Guidelines For Strategic Planning (Chapter 12)
Individual Human Resource Record
Job Description Questionnaire
Management Skills Audit (Chapter 10)
Meeting Action Matrix (Chapter 10)
New Employee Check List
New Employee Progress Report
On Site Patient Time Study
Past Employer Reference Check
Patient Satisfaction Survey (Chapter 15)
Patient Visit Time Study (Chapter 3)
Payer Performance Table (Chapter 9)
Performance Evaluation Report
Performance Standards Worksheet
Phone Tracking (Incoming calls)
Physician's Retreat Questionnaire
Pre-surgical Financial Arrangements
Problem-Solving Worksheet (Chapter 8)
Productivity Tracking Form
Request For Time Off
Risk-Opportunity Matrix (Chapter 8)
Rooming Matrix - Patient Prep Standards (Chapter 5)
Sample Bio Sketch (Chapter 10)
Sample Discharge Letter (Chapter 6)
Sample EHR Project Timeline Schematic (Chapter 7)
Sample Job Description (Chapter 2)
Sample Performance Standards Worksheet (Chapter 8)
Sample Organizational Chart (Chapter 11)
Staff Survey - How Does Management Rate (Chapter 10)
Team Leader Tips
Telephone Appointment Tracking (Chapter 3)
The Art of Delegation (Chapter 4)
Tracking Log Diagnostic Studies (Chapter 6)
Training Monitor (Chapter 4)
Twelve Point Office Efficiency Test